"You would be wise to please me, Tanya."

Luke caught her tilted chin in his large, powerful hand, his eyes lazily fixing on hers. "We don't always observe the conventions on these islands, Tanya, as you must know. If a man likes to feel he owns whatever he sees, there are very few who would challenge him."

"Well, you don't own me, Luke Harrison!" Tanya spluttered. "And if you think you can just walk into my bedroom unannounced, then you had better think again. You're not lord of all you survey."

His grip on her chin tightened. He was so near she could breathe the sensuous smell of his big body.

"Not exactly," he mocked. "But we also have certain codes and no other planter would go against me. You'd do well to remember that."

Marriage Impossible

by

MARGARET PARGETER

Harlequin Books

TORONTO • LONDON • NEW YORK • AMSTERDAM
SYDNEY • HAMBURG • PARIS

Original hardcover edition published in 1978
by Mills & Boon Limited

ISBN 0-373-02260-3

Harlequin edition published May 1979

CHAPTER ONE

AWAKENING in the first light, Tanya heard the familiar sound of a rain shower pattering dully on the patched-up roof above her head and the restless roar of the nearby sea as the huge combers broke ferociously over the reef.

It couldn't be more restless than herself, she decided wearily, thinking longingly of nights in the past when she had slept soundly until long after dawn had filtered through the cracks in the splintered cabin walls, removing the last traces of drowsiness from her eyes and filling her with the joyful promise of a new day. She never slept late, but never before had she known such a surge of relief to throw off the mosquito net and creep, ghost-like through the drooping door to watch the grey world change into gold as the rain stopped and the sun rose over the hazy blue horizon.

Outside, the outlines of the island were slowly taking shape, a gentle island, rugged yet green, rising softly from the sea, its surrounding reefs flashing white with leaping surf. The surf could be noisy, yet nothing that broke the all-prevailing silence was abhorrent to the ear as the sounds were all natural ones. Behind her the soft, fluted notes of the woodpigeons came from the green arbours of the trees and the wind whispered quietly through the tall, feathery branches of the palms as if urging the other birds to join in. Soon they would, like some heavenly chorus, as if their small, variegated breasts were about to burst with the very pleasure of their song. It was really wonderful but at this moment almost too much to be endured.

Sighing, Tanya turned away, not bothering this morning to run down to the beach, to immerse her slim young

5

body beneath the cool, refreshing waves before dressing. Instead she went back into the cabin, carelessly pulling on a shirt and dusty jeans before making herself a cup of coffee with the last precious dregs from the tin. The gas was getting low, too, and the kettle took a long time to boil. Eventually she grew impatient and made her coffee while the water was barely more than lukewarm, so anxious was she to be gone before Tui and his wife emerged from the shack they occupied at the rear of the cabin. Their silent enduring sympathy would be even worse to bear than the birds. Since Tanya's father had died, a week ago, the elderly natives seemed to regard her as someone who must be watched over carefully. She puzzled about it, but could only conclude that they were nervous that the shock of her father's sudden death might cause her to do something rash. Much as she loved them she felt she couldn't take much more of their unaccustomed fussing.

Without waiting for anything to eat she escaped as quickly as she could, climbing a little way up the mountain behind the beach, the mountains which formed the backbone of most Pacific islands. Mynah birds squawked as she passed and occasionally a mongoose darted across the path as it wound between forest and the odd patches of open land. Tanya walked until there was only hill and valley, earth and sky, space and stillness, then, as the sun grew hotter, she slid back down among the banyan and coconut palm, the lemon trees and frangipani, the tiered banks of flowers to the shore and the wild rolling surf.

Something pagan in her revelled in the heat even while she was unhappy. This morning the sun was really hot and the first early stirring of wind had dropped to a light, scarcely discernible murmur. A perfect day, she thought sadly, as she wandered along, aimlessly pushing the pale gold sand with bare toes. A skeleton of a tree, bleached white from continual exposure, jutted out of the sand and she sank down on it listlessly, her eyes moving slowly over everything, alive only with a suffering frustration. Here was a beautiful world, one of green and blue, white-capped water, of beaches, lagoons, reefs and hazy, sun-touched horizons—and she could be forced to leave it!

It was fantastic, the sea such a shimmering blue, the island a dazzling emerald gem, the reality not to be outdone by any holiday brochure. She loved it, and it was impossible to believe it might become a prison, as Tui said. A prison because now that her father was dead the only other people on Karowi were old and would provide little company for a white girl on her own. And the only way out was through a narrow, turbulent channel, cut jaggedly through the live coral of the treacherous reef.

Tanya hadn't lived here permanently for over two years without learning how to manipulate a canoe, but the only time she ever took one through the cruel, gaping jaws of that entrance was when the copra boats called. Then she always had some of the islanders with her. Most of the captains of the copra boats had known her father. A foolish writer, had been their none too private opinion, who had chosen to settle on a practically uninhabited coral atoll. When he had managed occasionally to have something ready for his publisher they had collected it, waiting patiently while Tanya made the hazardous journey through the reef. Afterwards they had posted whatever material she passed them. Then, maybe months later, they would be back with desperately needed supplies. These would be paid for from the cheque Vivian Willis mysteriously arranged to have paid into a bank at the nearest point of civilisation.

It seemed tragic that the last boat had called only the day before Vivian had been taken ill and suddenly died. Tanya suspected it had been his heart. Tui had agreed with her amateurish diagnosis and inclined to blame himself, but it had all been over so quickly she doubted if there was anything anyone could have done. It had been an agonising experience having to stand almost helplessly by and watch someone die, especially when it happened to be a much loved parent. For the first time she had found herself regretting bitterly that they had ever come here. Not until then had she fully realised the drawbacks of having no immediate means of communication. Even now it could be weeks before they saw anyone, even another copra boat.

Meanwhile, what could she do? Frowning, as if the question tormented her, Tanya dug her long-suffering toes deeper into the sand. It wasn't that she was frightened of starving. It was easy enough, if one's needs were simple, to lead a lotus-like existence on an island such as this. There was fruit and vegetables, the milk of the coconut and fish of all kinds there for the taking, but there were dangers she hadn't thought about, not while her father was alive. Then, when men had occasionally come to the island, he had been there to protect her. The mildest of men in temperament, Vivian Willis had been tall and deceptively aggressive to look at. He also carried a gun and, although he would never say where it had come from, she guessed Luke Harrison, whom she liked to think of as their interfering neighbour, had supplied it. It would have been just like him to have almost thrown it at Vivian and exclaim, 'If your unreasonable daughter won't see sense, at least you must!'

Last night, for about the first time, Tanya had done. A couple of rogues—Tui's own words—arrived. Fortunately Tui had seen them coming through the surf and bidden her hide. Perhaps because sorrow had temporarily mellowed her naturally rebellious nature she had obeyed. Later she had been glad when she had seen how they had wrecked the shabby interior of the old cabin, and while she had been furious to see how they had knocked old Tui about she had also realised just how endangered she might have been herself, if they had seen her.

Fortunately they had left, but she had no doubt that, sooner or later, there would be others. Even Tui, when he had recovered, had warned her as to what could happen if such men came again and looked more closely around. They might not always see people approaching.

'I don't know what I shall do, Tui,' she had sighed.

'Missy must think of a way soon,' he had advised, shaking his grizzled old head. 'You go home. It would be better.'

Tanya didn't want to think now of his advice, nor of anxious fondness at the back of his wise dark eyes. It was a good life, here on the island, a warm sunlit life which over the months had taken on a satisfying, familiar pattern. Everywhere there was the scent of flowers, the gentle trade winds, the velvet sky, the sun and stars, the mischievous seas. Why should she leave it? She kept insisting to herself that, after all this time, Cousin Lucy wouldn't want her, but it was, as she well knew, a feeble excuse. The truth was that Cousin Lucy belonged to a world which Tanya didn't want to know any more.

Her tawny brown head drooped as she remembered the first time she had come here. In those days her father had been fairly affluent. At least he had been able to afford a seaworthy yacht, even if it had been fairly old and not too robust. Tanya had been an excited fourteen-year-old, at home for the long summer vacation and just as eager for adventure as her tall, middle-aged father. He had set off to sail anywhere. Perhaps a trip around the world, he had said jubilantly, would supply enough material for half a dozen books. They had got this far, miraculously without mishap as there had only been the two of them, when the hurricane had caught them. How Vivian had negotiated the reef in the small boat they had carried and reached the island neither of them ever clearly knew. It might have been better if there had been some simple explanation as, once there, Vivian had declared that it must obviously have been pre-ordained and had never tried to leave it.

It had seemed pretty idyllic to the young Tanya too and she hadn't really tried to persuade him otherwise. Being sent back eventually to a remonstrating headmistress, to say nothing of Cousin Lucy, had been heartbreaking, especially as Vivian hadn't allowed her to return to the island until she was almost eighteen. He hadn't exactly asked her, even then, but he had written that he wasn't feeling too well and after that there had been no stopping her. Reaching here on a dirty old copra boat had been an adventure in itself, not one she had been over-proud of as she had arrived looking extremely disreputable and grubby, but it still brought a small sense of achievement.

'You're quite mad, child,' Vivian had groaned, but he had been so patently glad to see her in spite of his misgivings that Tanya had refused to go back.

Strangely enough if it hadn't been for their domineering, jet-set neighbour Vivian might have put his foot down and insisted she return again.

Their neighbour! Contrarily wistful, Tanya suddenly shaded her eyes with one small brown hand, but try as she might she could see nothing in the heat-hazed distance of white foam. No sign of the island he claimed to own, no sign of the powerful launch he handled with such careless expertise. Never had she thought the day would come when she might long for the sight of him!

She hadn't met Luke Harrison until she had arrived to stay here permanently, although Vivian had mentioned his existence. He came occasionally, interesting himself in Vivian's writing, playing a few hands of cards and exchanging news, leaving a few welcome provisions. It had annoyed Tanya somehow, even before she had known him, that he appeared to set himself up as her father's benefactor when Vivian strove so hard to be independent.

Apparently the mysterious Luke Harrison travelled to most places by plane, but as there was no landing strip on this island he was forced to use a boat. It had amused Tanya to see him arrive that first time soaked to the skin as the sea had been rough. It hadn't been so funny when she had taken another look and noticed how his wet clothes had seemed to accentuate his powerful, well muscled body. Then her mocking, gamin grin had helplessly faded as a totally alien emotion hit her. She hadn't realised then that for the first time in her life a man had made her swiftly aware she was a woman.

This had happened while she and Vivian had been conducting a week-long war regarding her return to England. Luke Harrison had literally walked in in the middle of it.

'You want to lay her over your knee, Vivian, and lay on

hard,' he had drawled. 'She wouldn't dictate to me!'

For that Tanya had never forgiven him and had done her best thereafter to keep out of his way. That day she had spat at him like a small, enraged animal, 'Just who do you think you are?'

'Tanya!' her father had improvised a hasty introduction, mildly pained that his daughter should conduct herself in such a fashion. Did she have to look so furious?

'Your daughter needs a lesson in manners,' Luke Harrison had rejoined curtly. 'One which you're obviously incapable of dealing out.' His eyes had gone over her with steady deliberation. 'If she were mine ...'

'But I'm not, Mr Harrison!' she had cried, incensed because so much was at stake and just as she had seemed to be winning his untimely arrival could remove all her advantage. Didn't he realise Vivian needed someone to take care of him? 'I've heard about you,' she exclaimed recklessly. 'You don't have a daughter, do you? You couldn't even keep a wife!'

His face went black then, hard as granite with a fury to match her own, and she had known, with an oddly quaking heart, that she had gone too far. She should have had the sense to shut up about his private affairs. Vivian shouldn't have told an indiscreet teenager like herself that his wealthy neighbour had divorced his wife for desertion, whatever that meant exactly. Staring at him, in a kind of suspended shock brought on by her own rash temerity, it occurred to her to wonder how any woman could have left such a man. He might be older than herself—at a guess somewhere over thirty, but she could see he was attractive. Too attractive! He made everything inside Tanya curl up tight. She could feel a fluid sensation, like one of heat, creeping through her veins and she didn't know what to make of it.

What she had said might have been unpardonable, and from the expression in his eyes it was, but it certainly seemed to do the trick. It had struck Tanya swiftly as he turned away that his late wife could be his one vulnerable spot. She had no personal experience of such things, but she had enough sense to realise that a man like Luke Harrison wouldn't take kindly to any form of rejection!

Surprisingly, when Luke finally departed, Vivian had given in and agreed to let her stay. It was almost as if her confrontation with Luke had made him aware that she had grown up during the long years she had been away. Now she was a young, spirited adult, misguided perhaps in tackling a man like Luke Harrison, but determined to speak her mind and maybe very able to fight her father's battles as well as her own. Against his better judgment Vivian confessed that he couldn't bear to be without some congenial company any longer and that while life on a desert island might be enchanting in many respects it could be curiously uninspiring if one had no one to share it with.

'Now that you've annoyed Luke,' he'd sighed, 'he probably won't come back, so I hope you're as good a conversationalist as he is.'

Which coming from anyone else might have seemed a strange sort of welcome, but Tanya knew her own dreamy, impractical father. The fact that she was an excellent cook and typist would weigh very little with him.

So she had remained and, as she had done as a child, found the island and their way of life very satisfying. It was an existence which might either enthrall or bore one; with Tanya it was the former. Looking after Vivian, keeping the rather tumbledown cabin tidy, growing and finding most of their food took up most of each day. On top of this she had found time to help Vivian with his typing, and although she didn't find his articles particularly inspiring it did enable him to get a regular flow of material away.

To her astonishment, after the way she had spoken to him, Luke Harrison did come back to see Vivian, but she usually made herself scarce when he was around, which wasn't all that often. She hadn't enjoyed the peculiar feeling that had attacked her on that first inauspicious meeting and was sensitively wary of facing him again. She had contented herself with occasional glimpses, these mostly achieved by peering through one of the many cracks in the rotting old cabin walls when he was lounging with her father inside. That such secret observations grew longer over the ensuing months she would have actively denied, but the cramp she sustained in her aching limbs didn't lie, even if she chose to disregard it.

Sometimes, she had thought, staring in one-eyed concentration through a crack, Luke appeared to have been fashioned from the same hard, cutting coral as the reefs, and she shivered when she considered her foolish rashness in defying him. When he smiled his teeth glinted white and when he frowned his eyes could smoulder dangerously, like they had done in one awful moment when she had fancied he had looked straight back at her. Once he had gone outside and called her name, wandering down to the shore as if searching for her, but when she hadn't answered he had lost interest and gone away.

When she had asked Vivian what Luke wanted he had merely said that Luke had wondered if she would liked to go sailing with him. Then she had felt strangely vexed that he hadn't persisted and sought her out, which of course had been ridiculous, seeing how she did everything possible to avoid him.

It seemed surprising how she had managed to steer clear of him until a few weeks ago. The sight of him striding towards her along the beach had been a distinct shock. His determination, which she had sensed at a hundred yards, had kept her standing there, freezing every instinct which warned her to run. Silently she had regretted the ragged pair of jeans she had worn. She had cut the bottoms off, well above the knees, but she hadn't sewn them up and she knew they looked dreadful.

She had tried to smile as he had reached her, with bright indifference, trying to subdue the startled beat of her heart. 'Long time no see!' she murmured lightly, with what she thought exactly the right degree of sophisticated sarcasm. Yet, unable to sustain his withering gaze, she had dropped her own to the sand.

'You've had plenty of opportunity,' he replied cryptically.

Then, even more dryly, 'Perhaps there's some message I haven't received?'

Tanya had the impression he knew the answer to that quite well. 'There's been none to send,' she said sullenly, her soft, wide mouth with its childishly full upper lip tightening. 'What sort of message were you expecting?'

'I've wondered when you would be ready to leave the island.'

Her blue eyes shot back to his face. 'Leave the island?' she echoed blankly.

'I must be slipping,' he mocked tautly. 'Unable to talk sense into either of you.'

'What you call sense we might interpret differently,' she had flared, not liking that he could still affect her oddly.

His mouth thinned. 'Living on an island certainly hasn't dulled the edge of your tongue!'

'Does it have to?'

'Tanya!' He had surveyed the lovely set of her proud little head on the slim throat grimly for a few tense seconds. 'You're sacrificing your life here. Vivian is wasting his time too, and you both know it.'

He had regarded her, obviously keeping a tight rein on his impatience, getting under her skin, forcing her to retort, 'He's not wasting his time, he's writing valuable articles.'

'Come off it, Tanya.' Luke clearly didn't intend sparing her. 'Vivian is good, but he's far from brilliant. He just doesn't have what it takes—and you don't need me to tell you that!'

Blindly Tanya stared up at him, longing to lift her hand and strike that hard, derisive face. If she controlled herself it was because she suspected he enjoyed arousing her most primitive feelings. 'His work sells. What better proof than that?'

The twist of his lips was regretful. 'I think I've handled one or two things badly, but your age presented difficulties. Not now, however, and of that I should warn you. A girl of twenty is a different proposition from one of eighteen. You ought to be living and working among other young people, not struggling to exist here on the bare essentials.'

His cryptic remarks did odd things to her breath. They spelt mystery, one she had no inclination to unravel. She pushed back her long brown hair as the wind teased it across her mouth. 'Am I missing so much?' she choked.

'Sure.' He had sounded decisive yet absent-minded at the same time, as his eyes wandered over her clean, flawless skin down to the shadowed cleft where her tight, shrunken shirt parted. 'You're missing valuable experience. You should be learning to grow up. Boy-friends.'

'I'm not interested.'

'Of course you are. All girls are. You should be out and about, going to shows, dancing the night away, sharing a little romance. In other words, learning to be a woman.'

'I've told you,' her voice came strangled with indignation because he could speak of such matters so coolly, 'I've told you I'm not interested!'

'If I didn't know women so well I might almost believe you,' he jibed, his eyes amused, 'but you weren't shaped the way you are for nothing. How old do you feel, Tanya? Can't you see time is standing still for you here? You might not like me for pointing it out, but one of these days you're going to wake up. Better do it while someone dependable is around.'

'Your opinion of yourself is better than mine,' she flung back, childishly defiant. 'I can see no point in a lot of silly questions to which you clearly know the answers.'

'I wasn't exactly putting questions, Tanya. I was simply attempting to draw your attention to the fact that you're a woman, but it seems it's going to take more than words to convince you.'

Grimly he had stepped nearer and while knowing she should run from him she had stood rooted to the spot, aware of his wholly masculine arrogance with a kind of irresistible fascination.

'You see,' he had said softly, as his arms had gone out to draw her to him, 'you're trembling. You're just as curious as any normal girl about the mystery of sex—and just as afraid.'

'I'm not! I don't intend having sex with you!' she had spluttered, taking him literally, her cheeks scarlet, her heart racing so madly she knew he must see it quite plainly.

'Oh, I don't intend going so far as that, not right away, anyway,' he'd quipped mockingly.

'We don't even like each other!'

His answer was to pull her completely into his arms.

'Liking need not come into it,' he stated sardonically. There, on the hot sands, under a burning sun he drew her closer and kissed her, a hard, sensuous kiss which went on and on. Tanya felt a dizzying brilliance rushing to every part of her body and thought wildly, I don't want this—this is something I'd be better without! It had taken all the will power in her mind to remain rigid in his arms when every other bit of her had screamed urgently for her to respond. Something inside her gloried that after the first few seconds he allowed her no choice as a relentless magnetism drew them together. She could feel the buttons of his shirt hurting her as his fingers dug deep into the vulnerable hollow of her slender back, moulding her to him while his other hand clamped the back of her head, holding her mouth to his until hers softened with her heightening emotions. In spite of the way she held back she knew she didn't fool him. Not in the least!

When he let her go there was a satisfied gleam in his eyes, an enigmatical mockery as he considered the dense colour of her eyes, the clear stain on her cheeks denoting shock. 'Don't persuade yourself, honey, you can turn your back on this kind of thing. When you're ready for me to come and fetch you just let me know.'

To let him stride from her along the beach that day had been one of the hardest things she had ever done. He had made her aware of her slumbering womanhood for the second time and she had known only a crazy urge to run after him—to beg him to kiss her again, to show her properly what it was all about! She had felt almost weak

from emotional desire. Shameless, she realised now, but
then it hadn't been something she wanted to deny herself.
When he kissed her stars had shot against her closed eye-
lids, her whole body floating tempestuously towards them
until she had been lost in a kind of fiery galaxy, only wanting more.

Hadn't Luke felt like this? she had wondered, staring
after him desperately. Didn't he realise what he had done to
her? Despairingly answering her own query, she recognised
that he had acted deliberately, with every intention of
forcing her to acknowledge openly what she was missing.
Yet while she did concede that he might have a point, how
could she consider leaving the island and her father merely
to go back to England, to selfishly devote herself to her own
interests? If she wasn't here to look after him he probably
wouldn't bother to cook or eat anything at the right time,
and he would take little notice of Tui or his wife. Without
someone to type his articles he would never sell them, and
he got little enough encouragement from his publisher as it
was. She might be trapped by her own initial foolishness
in coming to the island in the first place, but trapped she
was, in spite of anything Luke Harrison might say, she
must be prepared to make the best of it.

She hadn't run after him, nor in the last few weeks had
she seen him again. He could be busy on his plantation
or away in Australia enjoying himself, and he wouldn't
know about her father.

Tanya sat for another hour, strangely listless, disinclined
to move, thinking of Luke now rather than her father,
wondering how she could have imagined feeling as she had
done in his arms. Since then she seemed to have grown
immeasurably older, no naïve girl any more to be swept
away by a man's experienced passion. If death had served to
wipe out such evidence of her past foolishness then she
must have one reason to be grateful.

Eventually she trailed back to Tui and his wife and
watched them preparing a meal in their ancient black pot
which they always preferred to anything more sophisticated.

She shook her head when they offered her a share. She didn't feel hungry and the coffee was finished. Tui still bore the marks of his encounter with the two men, probably only his mass of fuzzy black hair had saved him.

'I'll have something later,' she hedged, when Tui's wife became more insistent.

She didn't fool Tui. 'Nothing much in your larder. Missy Tanya, for later. It's time to go, little one. I think you know.'

'Oh, Tui!' She leant against the cabin and her head fell. Her voice was like the whispering sigh of the softly moving fronds of the palm trees. Dismally she closed her eyes as if by doing so she could shut out the inevitability of her position. 'I know I must go but I don't want to. Maybe no more men will come.'

Tui shook his head, his face as near to firmness as it could ever be, 'You know that not true, little missy. More men will come, if not today then tomorrow, perhaps next week. I don' know, but come they will, and without someone like the boss to protect you, I fear for you.'

'We have other men?'

'The only other men on the island are old like myself and few in number. They only wish to live in peace.'

Yes, he was right. Bleakly Tanya turned her head away, gazing out to sea. Tui had been injured once trying to protect her—what right had she to involve his friends? Even if they would agree to helping her without her father and the vital supplies his earnings had brought where would she be? Just to love the island it seemed was not enough, yet how could she get away?

'The copra boat called last week, Tui. It won't be back again for some time.' Her last sentence was uttered on a mixture of hope and despondency. Without the copra boat there was no other means of getting off the island.

She wondered how Tui could have forgotten and was startled when he replied, 'I know how you love it here, Missy Tanya, but you cannot stay. This morning I send another message.'

'Message!' Tanya went pale, her eyes widening apprehensively.

'Yes, missy. I send to big boss, Mr Harrison. He come for you.'

Luke Harrison! Tanya stared at the old man despairingly. 'I don't want to go with him, Tui. How could you have done such a thing?' She didn't ask how the information had been relayed. It was one mystery she had never understood. It happened, it was possible, she knew. Like the drumbeats of primitive peoples, black magic rituals, no longer practised but never forgotten, stored indelibly in the heart and blood. No tangible, explainable thing, but there to be drawn on when a need arose. Tui had no equipment, not as the white man would understand it. An islander many sea-bound miles away would have none either, but Luke Harrison would be given the message. 'You know Mr Harrison doesn't care for me!' she protested further, as Tui didn't speak.

Tui merely shook his head again as if not able to work out how such a consideration came into it. 'He is the only one,' he replied stolidly. 'Long time ago he said if any trouble to let him know. I send after your father die, but then he was away.'

'I see.' Heavily Tanya moved her tawny head, wishing he had still been gone. It pained her to realise Tui was right, Luke Harrison was the only one. It was unfortunate, but simply the grim truth. They had no other friend, although she doubted Luke would call himself that, now that Vivian wasn't here any more. It was frightening to feel so alone, but she must make the best of it. Perhaps if she buried her pride and was pleasant to Luke he might lend her money to get back to England. She might not need to borrow that much as she did have a little of her own. It might even be possible to cable Cousin Lucy and have money sent out, only Lucy might not be able to afford it.

'Missy—look!' Tui broke excitedly through her anxious meandering. 'I think Mr Harrison come now. You see, through the reef?'

Tanya didn't want to look. She didn't need to, she knew exactly what he would do. Outside the reef he would drop anchor, using all the careless knowledge of his long experience. He would come in on a canoe, displaying a similar expertise. He was good at it, he would be here any minute, and she didn't feel like facing him!

Tui was watching his progress and she didn't want to look at Tui either, to see the open admiration on his relieved old face. Approval at the way Luke Harrison managed everything. Panic struck Tanya as her thoughts began to whirl chaotically. He hadn't managed her yet! Nor did he have any promise of her co-operation. She couldn't stop him coming for she had no rights on the island, but neither did he, not here or anywhere else, so far as she was concerned.

To run would only be childish and she didn't intend to, yet she wasn't able to cope with the blind fear that took hold of her completely. Her feet took wings as with a muffled cry she turned and fled even while she realised she couldn't hope to escape indefinitely. Tui would know where she was, if that approaching devil didn't. Luke Harrison might be furious at her unpredictable behaviour and go. Tui only wanted her safety, she knew, but he didn't seem to understand that Luke might not want her. The thought was so humiliating she couldn't possibly stay to hear him tell her so.

But she regretted running when, a few minutes later, she heard him crashing through the undergrowth after her, shouting her name. 'Come here, you stupid little fool!' he shouted curtly, 'or do I leave you to the next marauding tramps who chance to come this way?'

Tui must have told him! Naturally he would; he had had no other choice. Nor had she, really. Her breath tearing from her exhausted body, she halted in her tracks, allowing Luke to catch up with her. It had seemed imperative that she make some kind of stand, now she was aware it had been a complete waste of time. Miserably she watched him negotiating the mountain track with long, pantherish strides. It was from here, high up behind the cabin, that she had many times observed him entering the lagoon, every inch of him steely hard and impatient.

He halted within a few feet of her, surveying her dishevelled, dirt-streaked face, and she stared back at him from defensive eyes which looked like two blue smudges stamped on her defiant face. If she had expected at least a little sympathy because of her father, she didn't receive it. Luke covered the remaining distance between them in seconds, gripping her slender young arms below the shoulders, almost as if he would like to have shaken the life from her.

'Always you have to prove you're an untidy, uncontrollable brat,' he ground out, his curious green eyes blazing, 'but don't expect me to continue the spoiling!'

'I didn't ask you to come!' she almost shouted at him, her own temper rising above the incessant ache in her heart. Sorrow had been her constant companion for days, she hadn't thought there was room for any other emotion. Now she felt her anger surge as, unsuccessfully, she tried to wriggle from his cruel grasp. 'I didn't know Tui had sent for you!'

'Who else would he send for?' he grated, his hands moving implacably to her shoulders, holding her still.

She fixed her eyes woodenly on the strong set of his neck, brown and bare against the cream silk of his shirt. 'I don't know why it had to be you,' she retorted stubbornly. 'It's not as if we've seen all that much of you!'

'I've kept in touch,' he corrected hardily, his fingers tightening so that she felt their impact as if against her naked skin. 'That last time you didn't give me the impression that you'd like to see me again. Not that a kid's opinion matters, one way or another.'

'I'm not a—a child!'

His eyes glittered dangerously. 'I can recall one occasion when I might have agreed with you.'

Tanya's cheeks flushed, yet she forced herself to look

at him steadily, to retort rather idiotically, 'I'm grown up all the time!'

His well cut mouth curled with sarcastic amusement. 'It could have been better if you'd drawn my attention to this before. Then you might not have been quite so alone when your father died.'

If she didn't exactly get his meaning, he left her in no doubt that he meant to insult her. Her blue eyes, the only definite colour in her shocked face, blazed. 'You might be little different from the men who came here last night!'

'A little more delicate, perhaps,' he mocked, 'but with the same aim in mind. You add up to something called temptation, Tanya, if you did but know it.'

To talk like he did, at a time like this! Not one word about Vivian! 'I think I could hate you!' she cried.

'Just so long as there's nothing definite. You could be deluding yourself.'

Her breath shallow again, she stared up at him. 'I think I'd be wiser to keep out of your way.'

He mocked her then, if his voice was a shade more indulgent. 'The paths of wisdom are invariably dull, Miss Willis. No one of your age should stick to them consistently. At least when a man's angry you know you have his attention.'

'I'd rather do without yours, thank you.'

'But you have it, whether you like it or not. Tui's message made sure of that, but before we go on to discuss your future in depth, Tanya, I suggest we clear up here first and get back to my domain.'

His place! She felt trapped, as if walls were rapidly closing in on her. 'You're jet set—Vivian said so. You can't want me!'

'Just stop right there!' His hands, which had began to relax their ruthless hold, tightened once more. 'We'll take one thing at a time. Jet set can mean many things, not all of them bad. Learn not to judge so precipitously. And no, I don't want you particularly, you or any woman, although

I'm not immune to the usual biological urges. From these I won't promise to protect you.'

'Then ...'

'Don't interrupt. I'm quite sure you have your own means of self-defence, but I hope I haven't sunk so low as to be no longer conscious that I have responsibilities in some directions.' He paused and when he spoke again she could tell nothing from his expression. 'I promised your father I would see you all right if anything happened to him, and I don't intend going back on my word.'

CHAPTER TWO

TANYA'S face whitened. If Luke Harrison hoped to shock her from prevailing apathy he was succeeding better with every sentence. 'My father asked this of you?'

Luke's mouth thinned. 'Don't put too much emphasis on that last word, little one. I'm all you have. Who else would he ask? There was no one, so you needn't pretend such horror and despair. We didn't go into details as obviously Vivian never expected anything would happen. And for my part he might never have agreed to what I have in mind.'

What did he have in mind? Her numbed brain couldn't take this in. 'Did he—did you, I mean, ever imagine he would go as he did?'

Her voice was barely discernible and she saw Luke's suddenly detached grimness. 'The situation was open to such a possibility, Tanya. Even you must have been aware of this. The whole set-up was crazy, and has happened before.'

'You believe,' she challenged hoarsely, 'there should be a law to stop people living as they like?'

'There are more than enough rules and regulations as it is, but there could be something to stop men committing what almost amounts to suicide. Protecting people against themselves, I believe it's called.'

'Daddy must have been aware of the risks. He must have made his choice,' she managed raggedly, aghast at the hardness of Luke's tone.

'Was he really in the position to take such decisions,' he asked coolly, 'with you to consider? I'm sorry about your father, Tanya, but don't ask me to admire him in this.'

She could have wept with indignation. 'He wouldn't want you to. He knew he didn't have to worry about me, that I can easily go back to England.'

'Which won't be as easy as it sounds, and well you must know it. The first thing, however, is to get you back to my place. We'll discuss the next step after that.'

Tanya closed her eyes for a moment against his sweeping appraisal. He was as determined as Tui that she should leave. Would it be the last time she would ever stand here looking out over the vast Pacific Ocean, with the afternoon sun bright and the sea a vivid sparkling blue? Would she never sleep again under a darkening sky with only the gentle wash of waves on the soft shore to break the silence? Her face paled tragically as she thought of her father, how lonely his grave would be when she was gone. Almost overcome by a sudden weakness she swayed. She would have fallen as Luke's hands left her if he hadn't caught her as he turned away.

Swiftly, taking no notice of her anguished protest, he whipped her up into his arms. 'Once,' he muttered grimly, his keenly compassionate glance well aware of her shaken condition, 'I was good at games. My old deftness still comes in handy.'

'Put me down!' she gasped feebly, yet not really wanting to leave the comfort of his broad chest. She had forgotten how soothing it was just to have someone to cling to. Even Luke the enemy was better than no one. A shiver went through her arousing a curiously unsettled feeling, a faint guilt that in the circumstances she should be able to find comfort in anything. It gave her the strength to struggle.

'Be still!' Luke ordered sharply. 'Your weight isn't bothering me, if that's what you're worrying about. You haven't learnt the first thing, have you? Not even that you have your limitations, the same as most people.'

Those who didn't would include himself! Defiantly Tanya opened her eyes, but whether she encountered the brilliance of the green-shaded trees or his glittering surveillance she never knew as her long lashes fell swiftly again. New sensations seemed to be crashing down on her when she least wanted them, and the man who held her just didn't seem to care that she had no strength left to fight him. She was no match for Luke Harrison and it was humiliating to know he guessed it. She was going to be forced to accept his charity. This might have been bad enough without being certain he was going to demand quite a lot in return. Some things she might not be prepared to give.

'Here we are.' If he had been aware of her nervous agitation in his arms he ignored it. Carefully, with an un-usual forbearance, he dropped her down by the cabin door, a faint gentleness still etching his face. 'Do you have any-thing to drink in there?'

Thinking he meant something for himself, she nodded stiffly, feeling strangely forsaken now that his arms had left her. 'We have some whisky, I believe. There might be some left. I'm afraid our supplies are low.'

'You had a boat in last week?'

'Yes.' How sharply he spoke! She was almost scared to confess. 'I had an accident on the reef coming back. I broke some bottles and the coffee was ruined as well. The lid came off and water got in.'

'So you've had nothing?' His voice was low but not un-duly fierce. 'Any brandy?'

'I don't think so.'

His arm went out as she took an unsteady step. 'I should have preferred brandy for you, but the other will have to do. If you can find it?'

'I don't want anything.' Blindly she pulled away from him. Did he think her grief unnatural, something to be dispersed with a glass of the strongest spirits he could find? He would consider this the most convenient kind of com-fort as it didn't involve him personally!

From his hardening expression it seemed she had been right in thinking he didn't enjoy the inconvenience of having her swaying about. 'We don't have all day,' he rasped. 'The sooner we get your father's things sorted out the better and you'll be more help if you're able to control yourself.'

'Daddy was all I had!' Trembling, she pushed the heavy

hair from off her hot brow, not concerned that Luke Harrison might see the tears in her eyes. She would let him know she didn't care for his opinion one bit. If she wanted to weep she would. How could he expect her to go through her father's things so soon? He couldn't be human! Yet, coming down the hillside, his arms had been kind.

With a bitten-off exclamation, as he bent a look at her damp face, he swept her inside the tumbledown building. Finding the lukewarm whisky, he half filled a glass and thrust it at her almost savagely. 'Drink this!'

Recoiling but realising numbly that she was in no fit state to defy him, Tanya almost snatched the proffered glass, choking on her first huge gulp.

He watched her cough and splutter with supreme indifference until she stopped. 'Sure Vivian was all you had, and he would have done well to have kept that in mind,' he said.

'What are you on about now?' Tanya found her breath again and glared up at him. She didn't like the whisky, but it seemed to give her strength. Courage enough to fight on.

'Look, Tanya,' he said harshly, 'suppose we leave any further discussion until later? There's going to be plenty of time to talk. Right now there are more urgent things, and unless you'd like to spend another night here we'd better get started. This lot, for instance,' he pointed to a pile of old books, mostly tattered. 'We'd better burn them.'

'Must we?' The fight went suddenly out of her, yet she couldn't bear what seemed like arrant destruction.

'It would be wiser,' he murmured, eyeing the lone tear that ran down her cheek. 'Once you know it's gone you won't be so keen to look back. Is there any small thing you'd like to keep?

'You're so kind!' she exclaimed, with soft sarcasm.

'Not as kind as I intend to be,' he echoed her tone exactly, 'but this too will keep for another day. Meanwhile, suppose we cut out the jibes and get to work?'

An hour later Tanya watched unhappily as flames devoured the remains of the cabin, the only home she had known for the past two years. There had been nothing much to save. Tui had taken the few odds and ends he had coveted, but Vivian's personal effects she had burnt. This, she admitted, was the only possible way, but not even her father's death had seemed as final as this.

'You should have kept the typewriter,' she said dully, to Luke. 'Tui won't know what to do with it and it was yours in the first place.'

'I've several more,' he shrugged his wide shoulders indifferently. 'It would be foolish to overload the canoe.'

He glanced at her grimly, aware that she had drawn into a world of her own. A world of pale sands and lonely waters, a beautiful yet sad place which she must leave. 'I might come back.'

'Perhaps.'

But his voice promised nothing and she knew it. Luke Harrison would never believe in sentimental journeys to decorate a last resting place. He was too strong, too full of animal vitality to waste time on such negative customs. Yet hadn't her father, only a few short days ago, been as seemingly healthy himself? He had never been a demonstrative man, she couldn't remember the last time he had so much as put an arm around her, but he had been here and she had loved him. The wind sighed through the tops of the palm trees, the same trees that had so often lulled her to sleep, and her heart was aching, about to burst.

'Come on!'

There was no mistaking Luke's abrupt command. 'I'm ready,' she gulped, for once almost welcoming his curtness as she picked up the bag which contained her few belongings and followed him without another word.

Her throat tightened as she climbed into the frail canoe, but it was not from fear. The dangers and excitement of reef-hopping had long been known to her and the shock and sorrow of the past week had already numbed her senses. When Luke gave orders she found herself obeying automatically. She seemed to have no strength left to continue resisting him. All she could do was fix her eyes on his powerful shoulders as he eased the breadth and length of himself down beside her. If he lacked anything in strength, she thought bleakly, the deficiency would be more than made up in will power!

'Ready?' he shouted, and her reply, if she gave one, was lost as the first of the huge combers whirled them about, lifting them, pointing them straight towards the wall of coral that made the reef.

Her dry throat wouldn't allow her to shout, but he apparently didn't expect an answer as he never so much as turned his head. If he had he might have seen her last tearful glance at the small group of waving islanders on the shore. Nor did she try to stop those few bitter, scalding tears as they mingled with the salt spray on her face and would never be noticed. Everything was gone now, swept away, like the last sighing breath of the night wind.

She sat very still after that, watching the giant waves with awe, knowing that, if she moved, the canoe might easily roll over. She watched tensely but without any real apprehension as Luke used his paddles and they skimmed lightly over the heaving waters to where the waiting reef loomed monstrously ahead. There was a point where the sea rushed through a narrow channel in the coral. It was only a few yards wide, but it was there that some waves would rush through without breaking. The art of getting over the reef without capsizing the canoe depended very much on the choice of wave and the skill of the boatman. The canoe had to be manoeuvred with such accuracy that it was caught on the wave crest at precisely the right moment. Always before it had been terrifying, but with Luke Harrison the thrill became greater than her fear. She sat poised, scarcely daring to breathe, gripping the sides of the frail craft so tightly she felt her fingers might easily break. Suddenly the canoe was lifted, then shot forward at an incredible rate, its speed almost beyond comprehension. They were through, and shudders of violent reaction were running visibly through her slight frame.

She was scarcely conscious of Luke guiding them to-

wards his small cruiser which was dancing fretfully on the
rougher seas outside the reef. The wind rose, bringing
angry squalls, and the water kept heaving. As Luke came
alongside a wave washed right over her, soaking her to the
skin so that she felt more like a fish when he lifted her on
board with her clothes clinging wetly to her.

'Down below,' he ordered quietly, 'you'll find towels.
Can you manage?'

'Yes,' she struggled from his detaining hands with determination, 'but I won't change. My clothes will soon be dry,
I know from experience.'

'You do, do you!' His voice was terse as, disregarding
her defiance, he swept the long wet hair off her face. 'Okay
then, just sit there and develop all sorts of things you'd be
better without. Steam drying in the heat can lead to
pneumonia.'

'Oh, all right!' With a mutinous wrench she escaped,
wondering if it was rage that made her pulse beat suddenly
faster.

'Here, you'd better have this,' he tossed her sodden
canvas bag after her. 'If there's nothing fit to wear you'll
find something in the cabin.'

Finding a dry shirt was going to be a problem. Everything in her ancient holdall was soaked. Kneeling on the
cabin floor, she surveyed the pulpy contents glumly. Blast
Luke Harrison and his everlasting efficiency! What did he
really care whether she caught pneumonia or not? Men got
some peculiar things on their conscience, but why should
she get on his? If it *was* conscience that had prompted him
to make this difficult journey today from his home. He owed
her nothing and her father had certainly never done anything for Luke which might have put him in their debt.
That he was a hard man, not easily moved to ready sympathy, seemed to make it all the more mysterious. The hard
initial struggles of the islanders, their deprivations, their
indomitable efforts to survive might have been bred into
his very bone. But unlike the true islanders there was noth-

ing really gentle about him. His wife, who might have softened him a little, was gone.

A thought struck her strangely. He had been divorced, but could he possibly have married again? It was possible —wasn't he still a youngish, virile man with more than a hint of sensuality about him? Even Tanya in her innocence was aware of this. Yet if he had taken another wife and not mentioned it to her father, then surely Tui would have known. There was a grapevine of secret communication which the islanders used. The same mysterious means which had brought Luke Harrison to her aid, and seldom lied.

Because the thought of Luke being married again disturbed her she wrapped herself quickly in a large dark blue towelling robe she found on a nearby peg and took her wet clothes back on deck again to dry. The robe, which she suspected scarcely reached Luke's knees, trailed around her feet, but she didn't worry about it over-much. It did, after all, cover her completely, even if it didn't have buttons. In the mood Luke was in he probably wouldn't notice if she wore nothing at all!

About this she was forced to change her mind when she almost immediately bumped into him again.

'What the ...!' he broke off, continuing half under his breath as he turned quickly and saw her. 'I thought you'd be going to rest. You do choose your outfits,' he drawled, his mouth relaxing slightly. 'Couldn't you find something more suitable among your own things?'

'I'm sorry,' she muttered, trying to be coolly polite and not to notice he had discarded his own damp shirt and looked too blatantly masculine for easy viewing without one. 'I had to wear something while my own clothes dried. I promise your robe won't be ruined.'

His eyes lingered consideringly over her and, because his close brooding glance unsettled her a little, she put up her hands and began to plait her untidy hair, which confusingly only appeared to deepen his interest in certain parts of her anatomy. His was an impersonal, mocking dis-

section as if he imagined she acted deliberately to capture
his attention and, her cheeks flushing scarlet, she hastily
dropped her arms, leaving her hair to flop over her face
again.

'My robe won't be ruined, Tanya,' he hastened dryly,
'but it mightn't be good for me to remember how you
looked in it each time I put it on. Women have an underlying perfume of their own which both tantalises and
clings.'

As before, she felt he could be deliberately trying to shock
her from her bemused state. He would know of these things,
of course, having been married. It obviously didn't make
him tremble, as it did herself, even to think of it. Foolishly
she clung to the only form of protection she could think
of. 'You regard me as a child.'

Incredibly his mouth twitched, 'Not dressed like that, I
don't. In fact I haven't for quite some time, but that's another story.'

Uncertainly she glanced up at him as she slumped against
the nearest support, huddled in a small heap, arms clasped
around her knees as if unconsciously seeking to protect
herself. 'You can talk as much as you like, but I don't suppose it matters how you regard me as I'll soon be gone.
Maybe some day I'll be able to repay you for all your
trouble.'

'I have no doubt,' he agreed suavely, his eyes leaving
her at last to scan the darkening sky. 'There's already
something I have in mind. I guess it's good business to consider possible returns.'

In spite of herself Tanya felt cold with apprehension,
hollow with a strange disappointment. So he hadn't made
this journey today from out the goodness of his heart.
Didn't he realise how little she had, that she could offer
him practically nothing? If it was simply some small service
he was after then she would do her best to oblige, although
his hard undertones made her shiver. 'If there is anything
you only have to ask,' she promised formally, if rashly.

She didn't feel over-rewarded for her generosity as he

laughed, his cool glance playing sardonically over her before he turned his attention to the wheel again. Unhappily bewildered, she tried to concentrate on the bouncing waves rather than his broad, inflexible shoulders.

The green shape of the island loomed suddenly against the blazing tropical sunset. Like the one she had just left behind she could see the dark, feathery palm trees on the skyline, where the reds and pure golds merged with the greeny blues of the sea. How much of this island did Luke Harrison own? If not all it must be a good part of it, and it was much larger than Karowi. Her father hadn't owned anything, but Luke Harrison was a man who would want the deeds to everything he touched. Even girls like herself might not escape easily.

Her eyes went to him again, something about him drawing her attention more surely than her new surroundings. There was something dark and forceful about him. She tilted her head as though to study him better and her glance slid over his hard, handsome face. It went further. She supposed he would have what was commonly known as a splendid physique. Confused, her eyes flew back to his face and a familiar tremor ran down her spine as she met his glinting green ones. She liked to think she was immune from his undeniable attraction, but she wished she could be sure. Her small face was intense as some fearful emotion clutched her heart. His years of experience must have taken him miles beyond her own tentative, girlish dreaming. Never could she hope to match him, nor would she ever try, in spite of the hard knot of peculiar excitement he could arouse in her throat when he looked at her.

He was studying her in silence, his eyes ranging over her, and she hastily controlled a near sob, not knowing why she should feel so disturbed. If she cried he would say something cynical again and she didn't want that. He could be cruel, not believing in sparing her unless it suited him and she didn't yet feel able to stand up to him. Quickly she averted her tawny brown head to concentrate on the fast approaching island lest he should recognise her sharp panic.

Expertly, as he did everything else, Luke brought the boat alongside the wharf. Tanya thought it must be his private landing stage as there wasn't much else. There was a low stone wall which she was barely able to make out through the darkness. Beyond it gardens and lawns ran down to the beach. She couldn't see the house very well, but it appeared to have a large, menacing shape to it which made her imagine, stupidly perhaps, that the man and house must be alike.

'In another few minutes,' Luke said dryly in her startled ear, 'we might have company, so I'd advise you to get out of my robe.'

'Oh yes.' She flushed with mortification that he had had to remind her and she gave a funny little gasp as she practically dived down below. The cotton of her shirt and shorts was drier but uncomfortable with salt and sand and she regretted not having thought to rinse them out. Their roughness scratched her skin, but she dragged them on, thrusting his robe back quickly in the cupboard, as if glad to have it out of sight. The things Luke said so casually had an ability to hurt, but she must not get too sensitive. His lanced remarks and arrogant way of speaking might be habitual rather than directed at her personally. Possibly, after his unfortunate marriage, he addressed all women this way. If he seemed occasionally to be aware of her as a woman, maybe this applied to all the female sex apart from the very young or old. He wouldn't waste time on a girl like herself when he probably had the pick of so many more glamorous ones.

When she joined him again, sure enough a small group of islanders had gathered. By the light of a kerosene lamp Tanya could see them staring at her, their dark faces full of the warm interest that so marked these islands of the Southern Seas. Anxiously at first she gazed back then slowly relaxed, feeling contrarily more at ease with them than she did with their boss. On Karowi there had been only a few dozen people, including Tui and his wife, who had lived near the cabin and helped when needed, but she had grown to like the dark-skinned islanders very much. These people stared at her, but they seemed to find nothing odd in her untidy appearance. Their glances were kind, as if they understood about her father and were sorry. She could almost feel their sympathy reaching out to her and her deep blue eyes filled with tears as she reacted sensitively to it.

'Come on.' Luke's long, level glance took it all in, the tortured, frightened look of an over-reacting child. Tanya felt the strengthening, compelling force of his fingers as he gripped her arm, the encouraging, reassuring murmur of his voice in her ear as he thrust her through the milling throng.

He paused, a brief second, to give a few curt orders and they dispersed like so many shadows.

'Will they bring my bag?' she asked anxiously, as they walked through the lovely old tropical garden towards the house. Giant moths made for the lamp Luke carried, their wings flickering white against it, their eyes glinting red, but she was used to them and took no notice other than to lift her free hand to them when they brushed against her hair. Entangled in hair they could be almost impossible to dislodge. 'I shall need my clothes,' she added, when he made no reply other than to tighten his grip on her slim arm.

He murmured something non-committal which she took to be assent as she was positively rushed along by his side. It was dark, there could be no sense in lingering, but she wished he would shorten his strides. The house, too, looked dark with only a few lights where she had half expected to find them streaming and she paused nervously, pulling back from the hand that would have impatiently propelled her forward.

'What is it now?' his query was curt, so taut that she wondered if he reserved this special tone for her.

'Nothing,' she stammered illogically, stirring her lagging feet.

'If you're about to complain that you don't feel welcome, forget it,' he said. 'No one knew you were coming, with the exception of the few islanders who might have guessed.'

Swiftly they were over the doorstep into the dim confines of the hall, a great cavernous place, from what she could make out, and he was switching lights and calling loudly for a servant.

'Take Missy to her room,' he ordered, when one came. Then, to Tanya, 'Toma will look after you, she's very efficient. Dinner will be served later, but if you want anything now she'll bring it, you only have to ask.' He turned back to Toma. 'Is Miss Elizabeth around?'

'No, Mister Luke.' The girl paused. 'I think she still upstairs. She went to rest and has not come down.'

Luke made no comment and Tanya felt her throat go strangely dry. Who was Miss Elizabeth? He hadn't mentioned another woman, but he spoke of this one so casually that she must surely be his fiancée. He must be considering another wife. Tanya hadn't thought of this and felt suddenly so shaken she couldn't look at him. 'I didn't realise you had a fiancée,' she almost whispered. 'I'm sorry.'

He glanced swiftly, his eyes narrowed on her unconsciously dismayed face. 'I haven't got any fiancée. Perhaps,' he taunted mockingly, 'I wouldn't be so lonely if I had.'

'Oh,' she uttered, nonplussed, aware that in the course of one afternoon she had asked too many personal questions. Her pale cheeks flushed scarlet. He couldn't possibly be concluding, judging from her curiosity, that she was interested in him herself?

'I'll see you later, Tanya,' he said, turning away as if already he had lost interest and had more important things to do.

Her breath quickening, Tanya fled after Toma, up the wide staircase which curved and shone with all the depth and polish of fine old colonial wood that contrasted too painfully with the cracked, broken walls of the cabin she had left. She could see, now that the lighting was better, that it was a very fine house indeed and that it must be more than pleasant to live in.

Toma was darkly graceful. She might, in later years, grow fat, but now she was young and slender, her hair very thick and black and drawn neatly back against her neck. She ran a bath for Tanya and the luxury of the beautiful fitted bathroom was something Tanya found difficult to take in all at once. It was so long since she had had a proper bath that for several minutes she could only stand and stare at it, knowing she was giving Toma the impression she had never seen such a thing in her life.

She stayed in it far too long, delighting in the bubbly, sweetly scented water and vowing fervently, over and over again, that she would never again take such a luxury for granted. Finding a bathrobe hanging behind the door, she wrapped herself reluctantly in it. It seemed a bit unnerving that she should be compelled to wear bathrobes belonging to two different people in the space of a few hours, although this one, she could tell, would never be large enough to fit Luke Harrison. Inexplicably she hoped it hadn't belonged to his wife. Then, while she wondered whether jeans would be all right to wear to dinner, the bedroom door opened and in he strode.

'I was trying to calculate how long you intended staying in there,' he exclaimed sarcastically. 'I imagined you'd seen enough water for one day without having to wallow in more. Another five minutes,' he continued, without hesitation, 'and I intended hauling you out myself.'

'You wouldn't dare!' she flared up at him, her cheeks pink as her impulsive temper stirred. To make matters seem worse, the front of her robe was still half open and the gleam of her exposed skin caught his eye. He talked as if by rescuing her he owned her!

He might have read her thoughts. He came over, catching her tilted chin, his eyes lazily fixing hers. 'We don't always observe the conventions on these islands, as you must know, Tanya Willis. If a man likes to feel he owns much of what he can see there are few who would challenge him.'

'Well, you don't own me!'

'There could be worse fates for a girl in your position,' he jibed, regardless of her indignant stiffening.

'If walking unannounced into my bedroom means you're starting the way you intend to go on, then you can think again,' she spluttered.

'You remind me of a piece of furious flotsam attempting to defy the big combers,' he rejoined indifferently. 'Only don't try me too far, girl. I have a temper.'

Deep down she shuddered, reacting strangely. Afraid that he should guess, she retorted angrily, 'And you consider yourself a kind of god, lord of all you survey? Able to use your temper whenever you choose!'

'Not exactly,' he mocked, his grip on her chin tightening until her fragile jawbone ached and he was so near she could breath only the sensuous, faintly sweaty smell of his big body. 'We regard conventions to a certain extent and we also have certain codes, but no other planter would go against me, and you'd be wise to remember.'

Tanya's head was becoming almost dizzy from all the turmoil within her, but she did her best to stay calm. She would like to have flown at Luke Harrison, to have slapped his enigmatical face, to have scratched his brown skin until it bled. Aghast at the force of her raging inclinations, she shrank back from the strength of his hand, scarcely aware how it slipped, as if naturally, from her defiant chin to her nape where it gripped equally harshly. He would only conclude, if she tried to hit him, that the years on the island had turned her into a little savage.

'I'm going tomorrow, so I won't need to remember anything, Mr Harrison.' She made an effort to steady her voice. 'I think I have almost enough money for my fare. If I do have to borrow I'll certainly repay you.'

His grey-green eyes glinted. 'You aren't leaving anywhere tomorrow, nor the next day. I'd advise you to stop even thinking about it for a while. I don't intend lending you anything. You might never be in a position to repay.'

That this could matter to a man like him! Tanya's eyes rounded unwisely with contempt. 'I have enough to get me so far—from Dad's books. You can keep your money!'

'Where do you have it?' he sneered.

'In my holdall.'

'My servants have burnt it.'

'Oh, no!' She tried to say more, to slaughter him with words which wouldn't come, only now she didn't try to conceal the quivering resentment in her slight body.

His voice seemed actually laced with amusement, if emphatic. 'A few tattered clothes that I wouldn't allow you to wear, not even in this bedroom. The idea of money being hidden among them never occurred to me.'

Tanya had zipped it into an inner pocket, she conceded, but he was too smooth. She suspected he hadn't wished to find anything which might take away her independence on him. 'My books?' she gasped, suddenly considering a similar fate for them. There were only half a dozen, but they were all precious. It would be too much to bear!

Beneath the suave mask there was a watchfulness. 'They're down below. Those and the few other treasures you felt the need to keep. Rubbish, I might call it.'

'There's no sentiment in you, is there!' she flung at him furiously.

He stared down at her, his face carved from rock-hard masculinity. 'A little, perhaps, but I don't allow it to rule me. The islanders supply more than enough.'

'You mightn't be human!' she muttered fiercely.

He laughed in his throat, the lamplight glinting on his forceful face. 'Do you really doubt it? If you persist in wearing next to nothing you might soon have reason to change your mind.'

Startled, she flinched away from him and, almost as if he too was aware of an unpredictable tension building up between them, he suddenly let her go. Feeling relieved and resentful at the same time, she flexed her long slender fingers expressively. 'What do I wear—but what I can find, if you've destroyed all my clothes?'

'This is what I came to tell you,' he informed her coolly. 'You'll find the wardrobes in here full of clothes, some of which might be suitable. My sister-in-law's cast-offs, I'm afraid, but you're welcome to them.'

Dumbfounded, Tanya blinked. 'I can't just take someone else's clothes, even if she doesn't want them!'

Luke jeered, 'That's what I call sheer feminine logic. It's Hobson's choice, I'm afraid, unless you want to go around practically naked.'

The way he shrugged made her cheeks flame again. 'You can't make me!' The idea of wearing some other girl's clothes was at that moment curiously distasteful.

The tension was still there as he stated grimly, 'I have my own ways of dealing with obstinacy.'

Bitterly she acknowledged defeat, but not without one last effort. 'Won't your sister-in-law mind?' Surely she couldn't be the Elizabeth he had spoken of earlier.

He reached down, lean hands grasping her waist, impatient with her. 'She's had a family since she was last here. This certainly seems one way of settling a girl, something to keep in mind. She's lost a lot of her old restlessness and, as she lives in Australia, I don't anticipate seeing either her or my brother for some time.'

Because beneath his easy, contemplative gaze her heart lurched crazily, she whispered, 'I'm not married.'

'No, you're not,' his eyes studied her with a clinical thoroughness. 'You're a nice-looking child, though, and maybe it would be the best thing for you. Not that I set much store by marriage myself, it's a fool's game, but some women find it impossible to relax without that ring on their finger. However, rings are easily supplied and disposed of, as I soon discovered.'

He was talking way above her head, yet she couldn't somehow dismiss the personal angle. 'I'm not something to be made use of and then disposed of at the first opportune moment,' she quivered. 'Thank God you won't have anything to do with any possible marriage of mine!'

'Such recklessness,' he taunted. 'Wouldn't you be more alarmed if I were threatening to throw you out? Better the devil you know—eh? Outside you might be forced to accept something less than marriage with the first man to come along. Think of this, my small termagant, before you begin to berate me.'

She wouldn't say she was sorry because she didn't feel it, and she didn't need him to recount the dangers to a girl wandering alone in this part of the world. It wasn't as if she had other company or was on an organised tour. But there could be danger, too, in staying here with Luke Harrison, only, in his case, the peril might lie in her own vulnerableness to something within him.

His hands left her, but she still felt their odd, tingling warmth which helped to distract from the coldness his words brought when he said, 'I've to go out this evening, Tanya. It was already arranged, otherwise I wouldn't have gone. I'll be anxious as I can see you've decided to be un-predictable. I want your promise, for your own sake, that you won't leave the house. You can certainly try, but don't hold me responsible for anything that might happen to you. You couldn't get off the island without my permission, but I don't wish to have to go to the bother of rescuing you again.'

CHAPTER THREE

'I DIDN'T intend trying,' Tanya blazed up at him softly, dismayed for no obvious reason to the point of hurt that he should automatically think the worst of her.

She felt no better when he remarked dryly, 'Is it any use hoping there is some truth in that trite little statement? Women are good at saying one thing and meaning another.'

He sounded cynical, and Tanya found herself speculating suddenly about his wife. What manner of woman had she been? Why had she left him? A woman might either hate or love him but surely could never be indifferent. Of this Tanya felt certain, as a nervous little tremor ran right through her. There was an aura about him that was provoking and her heart flipped over. Her customary self-possession almost deserted her. Until now she hadn't realised, but she had the odd conviction that he could easily sweep her out of her depth, should he care to try.

When she didn't reply he went on to surprise her again. 'You won't be alone at dinner. We have an elderly housekeeper. She came with my grandparents, so you'll realise she's quite old and is really retired. Often she dines with me, but you could find her a little strange. All I ask is that you have patience with her. I'll endeavour to explain more clearly in the morning.'

'Of course,' Tanya agreed politely. She didn't altogether look forward to spending the evening of what could only be described as a trying day in the company of someone who sounded as if she might be difficult, but it was scarcely her place to say so. She couldn't very well object. Besides, it would be nice to have another woman to talk to, no matter what she was like. 'I'll do my best,' she said primly.

'Right then. I'll see you tomorrow.' Luke smiled grimly. 'Behave yourself.'

When the door closed firmly behind him she should have been glad, but somehow she felt terribly alone. She knew a quite urgent if ridiculous desire to run after him and beg him not to leave her. Where did he have a dinner engagement? There were no towns on this island, she knew. Was it with another woman, or some evening party where he would be ashamed to take someone as shabby and unsophisticated as herself? This, too, was ridiculous, Tanya chided herself, so soon after her father's death and her arrival here. The thought had merely flashed through her mind! It was, she supposed, because Luke was the only person she really knew that she had become loath to let him out of her sight.

'Luke ...!' she uttered his name aloud, her hand falling from the doorknob as she fought down the urge to shout after him hysterically. He would be gone; besides, she wasn't even dressed, and he might not look very kindly on her if she tore after him like this.

Dazed, she turned and wandered towards the huge old wardrobe, pulling open the door and surveying the array of gowns which hung there. Grasping the first one her hand touched, she took it carefully from its hanger. She would need undies, and the thought of fresh new ones encouraged her to pull out a drawer in a dressing table of an equally imposing size where she found a selection. Much of it looked brand new and not even in England had she ever possessed anything so fragile. Everything fitted perfectly except the lacy bra which was perhaps a little too tight, but as they all seemed the same size there was nothing she could do about it. The dress was a green silk and felt beautifully cool when she slipped it over her head, but it wasn't until she stared into the mirror that she realised how starved she had been for pretty clothes. Nothing she had ever had could compare with this expensive dress, of course. She had never been able to afford such perfection of quality or cut.

Feeling she was gazing at a stranger, she plaited her hair and felt immediately more familiar with herself again, although the effect was not so dramatic. She was pleased and rather surprised that constant exposure to sea air and sunshine seemed only to have improved her complexion. It had a satiny sheen to it that she liked. They hadn't had a mirror on the island, so perhaps she had some excuse for feeling oddly fascinated by her reflection. Almost she had forgotten how blue her eyes were and she noted, with a kind of bewildered interest, the winged brows above them and the way her hair lay, silky and heavy about her smooth brow.

The girl who stared back at her, biting her full lower lip, might have been someone else, and resignedly she turned away, remembering to pick up a light wrap before going downstairs. If she wasn't to get things straightened out with Luke tonight she might as well meet his mysterious housekeeper. Would she prove to be the mysterious Miss Elizabeth? Tanya wondered. Not that it could matter, one way or another, as tomorrow she would be gone.

Below there was a bowing Indian servant to see her to the dining room where a tall, thin woman was already seated at the table.

'Come in, dear,' the woman smiled brightly, darting a bird-like glance towards the hesitant girl. 'I hope I don't appear to be starting without you, but I'm too old to stand around waiting for someone who's late.'

'Good evening.' It sounded a bit stilted, but it was all Tanya could think of to say as she slid carefully into the seat the Indian servant pulled out for her. 'I'm sorry I'm late,' she made an effort to smile. 'I'm afraid I didn't know the time.'

'I'll tell Dino to put a clock in your room,' the woman frowned. 'I'm Miss Logan, you may call me Elizabeth,' she spoke again, abruptly. 'Luke has told me about you. I believe your name is Tanya.'

'Yes,' Tanya nodded nervously, 'Tanya Willis.'

'I told you, he told me!' Miss Elizabeth reproved primly. 'No need to repeat things.'

'I'm sorry,' Tanya meekly apologised again, as Miss

Elizabeth fell about her dinner as if she had had little all day. Tanya hadn't and, until a few minutes ago had felt quite hungry. Now she pushed the delicious crab omelette around on her plate and could scarcely face the roast beef when it arrived. Secretly she felt almost ashamed, for the beef was a rare treat, their diet on the island not having included such luxuries. They had fresh pineapple for dessert which she found refreshing. During the whole of the meal Miss Elizabeth didn't speak again, and after several abortive attempts, Tanya fell silent too, realising the woman was paying no attention to what she was saying. While this was not very companionable, it did give Tanya a chance to discreetly study her, but, apart from her abrupt manner, which might be no worse than Luke's, Tanya could find nothing very strange.

Over coffee, in a lounge as large as the huge dining room, Miss Elizabeth at last paid Tanya some real attention. Dismissing the hovering Dino sharply, she said, 'Luke also told me your father has just died.'

'A week ago.' There was a sudden lump of loneliness in Tanya's throat and she couldn't swallow any more coffee. Quickly she replaced her fragile cup in its saucer. Miss Elizabeth, she noticed, did the same, as if something suddenly interested her more than her food.

She didn't, however, press Tanya for more details of how it had happened. Instead she asked, with continuing abruptness, 'Are you going to stay here?'

'No,' again Tanya's voice faltered. 'Only perhaps until tomorrow or the day after. I'm going away.'

'You all go away, don't you,' Miss Elizabeth muttered querulously. 'First Rowena, now you—it's not good for a man to be without a woman. The servants don't understand how a woman can live with a man like Mr Luke and then leave him. They pester and embarrass me with questions. When you go I shall have to endure it all over again!'

Tanya flushed hotly. 'I'm not living with Mr Harrison,' she exclaimed, glancing indignantly at Miss Logan. She was staring vacantly into space as if she had already forgotten what she had been saying and she did, indeed, look rather funny. Even so, the sooner she made her position clear the better. Tanya decided firmly. Her position and Rowena's—if this was the former Mrs Harrison's name —were quite different. 'Mr Harrison merely brought me over from the other island,' she began to explain.

'You had to come from somewhere,' Miss Logan interrupted reasonably. 'You're a very pretty little thing and you mustn't think I'm not glad you're here. I'm leaving shortly, you see, I'm getting very forgetful. Just as soon as my sister can take me I'll be gone, and I wouldn't like to think Luke had no one to look after him.'

Deciding it might be wiser to ignore some of Miss Logan's remarks, or at least try to, Tanya replied politely, 'You must be looking forward to it?'

'I might be.' Cunning caution showed in Miss Logan's quick glance. 'I've lived here a long time, you see. I came as a sort of governess, nursemaid to Mr Luke's father. I saw him married, then Luke ...'

'But,' hastily Tanya swallowed, yet was unable to resist asking, 'he's divorced now, isn't he?'

'Yes, I do know, dear.'

'Didn't he have any family? I mean children?' This seemed to cause an actual pain somewhere in the region of Tanya's fast beating heart, and she couldn't think why.

'No, dear,' Miss Logan sighed, over sentimentally, 'I think this is where he went wrong. His wife didn't like the island and I expect she didn't want to be tied down. I had hoped to see the old cradle filled before I went, but she told me herself she didn't want children. His next wife, Luke says, won't be given a choice.'

'Oh,' Tanya murmured inanely, her cheeks confusingly hot again. 'Surely he wouldn't discuss—such things?'

Miss Logan drew herself up coldly. 'He certainly doesn't go on about it, but you can scarcely accuse a man of being indiscreet, just because he confesses to his old nanny that he would enjoy a family!'

'No, I suppose not.' Tanya tried to speak with equal coolness, but she felt her stomach churn.

'I taught Luke when he was young, before he went away to be educated,' Miss Logan said crossly. 'If I can't remember a lot of things I don't forget he was a charming boy. It's a pity boys have to grow up.'

'I'm sure you're right.' Remembering Luke's hardness, Tanya was convinced of it, but she was really trying to appease Miss Logan, who seemed mistakenly sensitive about his feelings. Luke Harrison was no concern of hers. How had his wife ever escaped, Tanya wondered, thinking of his hard arms and mouth, as mysteriously real to her as if she had just that minute endured them.

Suddenly, in the middle of her nervous ponderings, Miss Logan rose majestically. 'I'm going for a walk down to the beach, dear. It's such a pleasant afternoon.'

'But it's not. I mean, it's evening now, and dark. I don't think you ought to go out.' Alarmed, Tanya jumped to her feet. 'Why not stay here and talk to me?' she added persuasively.

Miss Logan didn't spare her another glance, nor did she even deign to reply, and Tanya stared at her in bewilderment. The servants had gone, probably they were having their own meal, and she didn't know where the kitchen was. Miss Logan was so tall and regal, it wouldn't be easy to gainsay her, but what could she possibly want on the beach at this hour? While Tanya was collecting her scattered wits, Miss Logan made a little rush through the door and, suddenly coming to her senses, Tanya grabbed a large bell off a table and rang it loudly. Within a minute Dino came running.

'Miss Elizabeth?' he asked, before Tanya could speak, and when she explained what had happened he didn't seem surprised.

'Not to worry, missy. I go after her. She is a little strange in the head in her old age, but not harmful.'

'I'll come with you.'

'If you like.' She had thought he was going to refuse and

was relieved that he didn't. 'Sometimes,' he nodded, 'Miss Elizabeth can be stubborn.'

Hastily Tanya picked up her long skirts and followed. Miss Logan hadn't got far. They found her standing at the bottom of the garden, where it touched the shore. She seemed to be watching the stars coming out as the darkness deepened and the moon rose, like a great yellow rim, just above the horizon.

Like a child who has misbehaved she allowed Tanya to take her back indoors, her shaky old legs stumbling even where the lawns were smooth and Tanya felt angry that Luke could go off calmly to see his friends, knowing the risk. Miss Logan might easily have walked straight into the sea!

Getting Miss Logan into the house seemed a simple matter—persuading her to go to bed was not! Long before the latter was accomplished, Tanya was exhausted and without help she doubted if she would ever have succeeded. By the time she got to bed herself she was so tired she couldn't think and fell into the first deep sleep she'd had without nightmares all week. In her dreamless state she didn't have a chance to wonder if this was what Luke had intended.

The next morning, long before she rose, he went out. Dino, when she enquired of him, said expressionlessly that his master owned many plantations of coconut and there was much work to be done. This, Tanya knew very well, but she also guessed there was little reason why he should remain away all day. It was evening before she saw him again and she was taut with frustration, her nerves raw.

He must have deliberately kept out of the way, she realised furiously. Stiff with anger, she dressed in the same green gown she had worn the previous evening, scarcely bothering to do more than roughly brush her long hair. She found him downstairs having a leisurely drink before dinner and looking well satisfied with himself. As Miss Logan was present Tanya couldn't manage to speak to him alone until after they had finished eating, which was perhaps all for the best as it did give her temper a chance to cool. Something she fancied Luke was perfectly aware of, judging by the glances of sardonic amusement he cast at her from time to time.

He was different this evening, a stranger in a dark suit and white shirt. She hadn't seen him in anything else but shorts with a shirt usually open at the neck, leaving half his powerful chest bare. Now he seemed almost a stranger, one whose light, enigmatical eyes considered her briefly but as if he knew every little thing about her. Dimly she suspected he didn't see her as a slender girl in an elegant dress, but as a little ragamuffin not really fit to grace his affluent table. It could be a long time, Tanya thought bleakly, before she attained the degree of sophistication he obviously looked for in a woman.

After the meal there was coffee, the thick Turkish kind that Tanya had found difficult to get used to, and it was served by the silent-footed Dino whose gentle unobtrusive ways she was growing to like. Immediately afterwards Toma came and escorted Miss Logan upstairs. When Tanya jumped up to help Luke waved her back to her seat again while getting up to close the door behind the two women himself.

'I want a word with you,' he said, but again they were interrupted when Dino came to remove the coffee tray. Luke spoke to him in his own language which she only vaguely understood, but she rather gathered he told Dino he didn't wish to be disturbed. There were so many different tongues on these Pacific islands, but most of the people spoke excellent English and Tanya had never bothered to learn anything else. She wondered now if Luke was trying deliberately to confuse her as Dino spoke English so well. As for wanting a private word with her——! Well, she certainly wanted a word with him, but she didn't care all that much whether it was private or not!

He sat down, not beside her this time, but opposite, where he could see her face. 'Did you sleep well?' he studied her casually, as though it were only morning and he had just met her over breakfast.

'If I hadn't,' she exclaimed, returning his glance mutinously, 'I might not have missed you this morning.'

'Dino tells me you had problems last night.'

Tanya disliked the way in which he neatly sidestepped the issue, but she answered him evenly enough. 'Not problems exactly. Miss Logan wanted to wander along the shore. It was as if she was remembering—other occasions, perhaps. I had to spend a little time persuading her to come in.'

'Quite,' his voice was clipped. 'It's for her own good. She used to be inordinately fond of the shore. At one time she had a huge collection of shells she kept adding to when she was out, but until a few months ago she would never dream of setting a foot outside after dark.'

Tanya, who had come to love the islands at all times of the day, felt surprised. 'Yet she must have lived here all her life?'

'Most of it,' Luke nodded, 'but it was people she saw more than places. She devoted herself, Tanya, to three generations of Harrisons. Can you wonder that I'm so keen to take proper care of her at this stage? This I mean to do until her sister can take over.'

Without thinking Tanya frowned. 'Isn't it rather strange that her sister is willing to take her on? They can't have seen much of each other.'

'It could be, although her sister has occasionally been here for a holiday so they haven't altogether lost touch. She's younger than Elizabeth and has just retired from a nursing career and, to use her own words, will welcome having something definite to do, as well as the company. Neither of them has ever married, so they're both quite alone in the world.'

Just as I am, Tanya reflected silently, feeling a little sorry for herself, for all the lone Elizabeths whose services were no longer required and who must be disposed of as neatly as possible. Perhaps as Luke Harrison had disposed of his wife, if the truth were known! He must be good at it to be able to talk of such matters so easily. Tanya, belatedly, lowered her tell-tale eyes. 'It's none of my business really.'

'But it's going to be. For the next few days, maybe weeks,' he assured her softly, fixing his gaze with determination straight on her face so that she was forced by the very strength of his personality to look at him again. 'I intend you should look after her until she leaves.'

Carefully Tanya sat very still, every bit of her warning she should tread warily. It was caution she would need in dealing with a man like this if she wasn't to emerge the loser. Not that she entirely regretted the swing the conversation had taken as it brought them indirectly back to her own plans. 'I'm sorry,' she replied, fighting him unconsciously in everything, 'but I must be on my way.'

His eyes glinted with an ironic smile. 'I wish you wouldn't keep repeating yourself,' he said patiently. 'You aren't going anywhere right now. For one thing you're in too raw a state so soon after your father's death and the best therapy could be to look after someone less fortunate than yourself for a while.'

'I don't ask for sympathy,' she flashed, 'but I don't think I deserve your toughening-up treatment! A little kindness could be more appropriate.'

'You would like that,' he mocked. 'A warm embrace, the tender, kiss me better sort of thing?'

'You only make fun of me!' she choked, her pulse racing.

'Don't worry,' he said smoothly, taking no notice of her obvious embarrassment. 'When you fled from me yesterday like a little wild animal I realised you'd been somewhat starved of tenderness, but all in good time. Tenderness has an unfortunate way of getting out of hand and I don't think you're ready to accept the consequences of such innocent yearnings yet.'

'I didn't want to be rescued!' she accused him, not for the first time desperate to hide her tormented nerves.

'Tomorrow I'll take you back and dump you!'

'Do you think I would mind?' She turned sideways, away from his calculating eyes, her face a pure, pale mask in the brilliant glow from the chandelier.

'Aren't you frightened of the men who would come and ravish you? You couldn't run for ever, you know.'

'And you would leave me to such a fate,' she cried contrarily, turning wildly back to him again, agitated beyond everything.

'You don't really believe it, do you? I might only be looking for the pleasure of rescuing you again, my little wildcat who needs taming.'

Not by you, every protective instinct protested, while deep down inside she suspected his intention. He would soon discover, if he tried anything, that she could indeed scratch, like the feline creature he so insultingly compared her with. It wouldn't be practical to return to the island, but she would rather die than confess it.

'Looking after Elizabeth won't be a very arduous task.'

If she hadn't known better Tanya might have thought his voice oddly persuasive. 'Couldn't you,' she murmured, feeling a desperate, if confused, urge to escape him, 'couldn't you find another woman? There must be plenty better qualified.'

His voice hardened, the faintly softer note gone. 'I want no woman here with probably every intention of marrying me.'

The conceit of the man! Yet her heart reacted again strangely. 'How could you possibly think that?' she exclaimed scornfully. 'No one would even know what you look like, or that you're—you're divorced until they arrived!'

He wasn't impressed by her stammerings and stuttering. 'You'd be surprised,' he countered dryly.

'I would have thought you more than capable of dealing with any woman's romantic inclinations,' she jeered rashly.

'But not willing to sacrifice the time and trouble involved, not when it can nicely be avoided. I've had enough of sickly sentiment, this is why I feel you'll suit me very well indeed. Your mind is quite stunned at the moment, quite incapable of imagining you're falling in love with me.'

Tanya stared at him blankly. He talked as if she were a robot, incapable of personal thought or feelings, to be programmed exactly to his requirements! He might be right in some of the things he said, though. She wasn't quite sure what she felt or wanted, other than that something about Luke Harrison affected her oddly. Self-protectively she sought to draw his attention away from herself. 'I can't see why you're so antagonistic towards my sex on the whole, especially as Miss Logan told me you aren't considering living alone permanently.'

'Elizabeth rambles. I thought you realised this is her trouble,' he said grimly. 'She's right, of course, that I do intend remarrying some time, but when I do it will be because I'm good and ready and for the right reasons. Not the result of a youth's mistaken infatuation!'

Was this what his marriage had been? 'I'm sorry,' she offered untruthfully, 'you've been unfortunate.'

His eyes glittered at her soft sarcasm. 'If I have been it's all in the past, but there are some lessons a man should never be too proud to learn.'

But he was proud, Tanya knew instinctively, as proud as the devil and arrogant for all his humble words. Words could mean nothing, nothing at all, but she mustn't worry over-much about the things he said with a smouldering to the back of his eyes which boded no good for her. 'You may not have made a success of your life,' she stumbled, 'but it has nothing to do with me. All I ask is to be let go. That you should give me some assistance which I'll repay. Surely, for a man in your position . . .'

Her voice trailed off as he slowly shook his dark head, his eyes narrowed as if he still considered her first sentence. Coolly he said, 'I liked your father, Tanya, even while he chose to live like an outcast and showed a far from responsible attitude towards you.'

'And you consider you are responsible,' she broke in, 'in keeping me here, a virtual prisoner?'

'Yes.' He was suddenly on his feet, ruthlessly pulling her to hers, his hands still retaining their grip on her arms as they had done the previous afternoon. 'Would I be responsible if I sent you back to the U.K. now, prey to the first man who looks at you?'

She flushed scarlet. 'You must think me very naïve!'

'Not exactly,' he conceded generously, 'but there are others who might think you are. Believe me, you could be hurt, physically as well as mentally, and I don't want this on my conscience.'

Tanya's temper was rising because it all seemed so ridiculous. Couldn't he see that she daren't stay any longer because of him! 'If you think a few weeks are going to change me, you're mistaken,' she cried, her eyes rising no further than the middle button of his shirt.

Luke said emphatically, as if he had definite intentions, 'I'll supply some of the experience you need, if you stop spitting at me like a sulky little tigress. Come, Tanya, we both need each other, if for different reasons. Why quibble about the odd point which doesn't suit you when you can be extremely comfortable here? You help me and I'll help you. What could be more reasonable than that?'

Her limbs weak, she glared up at him, confusion and anger colouring her cheeks to a tantalising pink. 'So not only am I to look after Miss Logan, I'm to supply you with some amusement as well!'

His mouth sneered, as if he suddenly lost patience with her. 'I'll guarantee you enjoy it as much as I do, and I have little time to watch you pretend to be shocked. I've had you in my arms before, remember, so I know you're not the frigid little iceberg you like to pretend to be. All women have a natural curiosity and I promise to go gently. What more do you want?'

What more indeed! Angrily she met his taunting eyes, as always having an insane desire to strike him. It's apparently a sheer waste of breath repeating myself! I don't appear to have any choice but to stay, but I might find an opportunity to escape, not matter what you say or do.'

'Don't try it,' he warned. 'Whatever you think you'll be safe here. Out in the big bad world you'd be on your own.'

'The thought doesn't deter me!' She tried to break free. 'How long is Miss Logan to be here?'

'Matter of a few weeks,' he held her with determination. 'No longer than it takes her sister to recover.'

'Then what?'

'You should try wearing blue, Tanya. Or shall I give you a sapphire necklace to match your extraordinary eyes? To-morrow evening I want to see you in a different dress, something a little more exotic, then we shall see.'

How she hated the cool, velvet depth of his voice, the way it sent shivers curling down her spine when he used it with such calculated deliberation. 'I asked you a question?' she gasped. 'What happens after Miss Logan leaves?'

'How you like to leap ahead,' he growled. 'My mind refuses to carry me so far. Since when did you begin troubling yourself so much about the future? You were content enough on Karowi.'

'That was while I had someone to look after me.'

He showed not a glimmer of softening. 'I'll look after you from now on, Tanya. You'll have no reason to com-plain. Come here.'

She gazed up at him, stunned to stupidity, as he drew her closer, her fringed eyes glowing like gems between the tips of her thick open lashes. The light struck his darkly tanned skin, his hard mouth set in lines of amused mockery as it descended gently on hers. Her breath mingled with his as she opened her mouth to protest and his arms encircled her completely. Then the pressure of his lips deepened until, softly helpless, she collapsed against him.

'See what I mean?' His warm mouth left hers so sud-denly she felt abandoned and the wild rose colour in her cheeks betrayed the passion and humiliation within her. His query, if this was what it was, was cynical, as if he understood her needs better than she did herself and was amused by them. Nor was he finished.

'Why the little tremor?' he murmured, intent it seemed to ask questions she couldn't answer. She felt her skin prickle where he trailed experimental fingers down her bare arm before putting her decisively from him. 'There might be ways,' he threatened, 'of making sure of your co-operation.'

What he meant by that exactly Tanya couldn't tell, nor dared she challenge him as her voice when she tried to speak didn't function. Her throat was too tight and she wouldn't risk him laughing at her, not after what he had just said. Instead her hand flew out to contact his cheek sharply, as she had longed to do since they had met, for reasons which seemed too multiple to name singly.

She wasn't going to apologise, but apparently Luke didn't expect it. He merely laughed, laughter that made his eyes glint and his teeth flash wickedly, as if her re-action amused him. 'You're going to need every bit of spirit you possess, but even then it won't be enough. I'll subdue you, my girl, supposing it's the last thing I do!'

Next morning, because she felt too upset and restless to stay in bed, she was up early and was surprised to find him apparently waiting for her when she came down to break-fast. Not that she wanted anything but coffee but, unlike the previous morning when she had been eager to see him, today she had hoped to find him gone. She had intended setting out on her own to explore at least some of the island to see if she couldn't formulate some kind of plan to escape. The sight of Luke leisurely eating his breakfast almost proved too much for her taut nerves. A feeling of unhappy dismay running through her, she stared at him blankly. Later Miss Logan would be about and she might not find it easy to get away.

He watched her walking over the polished wood floor towards him as if he was entirely interested in her pro-gress. It seemed not to have escaped him that she moved with much of the same fluid grace of the true island girl, her soft skirt fluttering gently about her long, slender legs.

He said astutely, 'You have the air, this morning, of someone who's made a fortune and lost it in the same few minutes. Can I help?'

'If that wasn't so funny,' she retorted tartly, slipping into her chair, 'I might scream! You wouldn't help me, I suspect, if I were drowning.'

'Well, you aren't,' he replied sensibly, 'so that's one theory we can't test, but I still think the sight of me confused you, and not because of last night. You've a very readable little face, Miss Willis.'

Her small, guilty start must have added weight to his suspicions, but she refused to give him the satisfaction of an open confession.

'I know women, Tanya,' his voice changed harshly. 'Give them an inch and they'll take endless advantage. However, the old cliché, once bitten, twice shy, has a lot of truth in it.'

She said quickly, 'I could also mention the one about putting your fingers into a fire. It's one's own choice.'

'I shouldn't have been surprised when I got burnt, eh? But very few people realise marriage is a kind of fire until they jump into it.'

'This can't always be the case,' she said scornfully, helping herself automatically to coffee. 'Anyway, I thought you would have been too smart to be caught by the kind of wife you've obviously had.'

'Be quiet!' His voice, usually low and even, apart from the odd inflection, suddenly thundered, regardless of Tanya's shocked, startled face. 'One more crack about my marriage or my partner from you and I'll thrash you within an inch of your life!'

'You wouldn't dare!' She jumped to her feet, her cheeks scarlet with a small fury which showed, although it in no way matched his. 'Lay one finger on me,' she cried wildly, 'and you'll regret it! I'll go to the police!'

'You'll have your work cut out to find them here,' he

sneered, but controlling himself, to her chagrin, more
easily than she did.

'I'll find somebody—there's always somebody!' Temper
almost getting the better of her, she turned, an unbalanced,
misjudged movement by which she managed to upset her
almost full cup of hot, milkless coffee. It ran like lightning
off the edge of the polished table on to her bare leg. 'See
what you've made me do!' she choked, childishly, as the
pain of it needled her skin with searing intensity.

'Sit up!' As she half knelt on the floor hugging her knee,
Luke was with her in a flash, crouching so that he could
examine the already reddening skin. Swiftly he rose, his
arms coming out to pull her up with him. 'You'll have a
sore patch, but there's little damage done, I think.' With
an obvious lack of sympathy he thrust her down again into
her chair. 'Stay there until I find a bandage. Dino will
bring one. I imagine your pride is smarting, too, but I can't
put anything on that.'

'An apology might help!' Tears, which were more of
resentment than pain, made her eyes glisten like damp
violets in the rain. 'To threaten me like that!'

'Did you think I would merely tease?' After ringing the
bell and instructing an anxious Dino, he turned on her
grimly. 'I know how feminine a woman feels to be given
a playful smack, but the sooner you realise I'm not here to
receive your impertinence the better. You've been spoiled
by your father and those doting islanders, don't expect me
to do the same.'

Dino returned with everything necessary to relieve her
stinging leg, if not her almost reeling head. She hadn't
thought her remark impertinent, it must have been the way
she'd come out with it. Sullenly she watched as Luke
dressed her leg lightly, confused that the touch of his
fingers should send peculiar, sensuous quivers through her
after all he had said. She only wanted to feel hate! How
she wished she hadn't given way to a wistful fancy to look
feminine this morning and put on slacks instead of a
frivolously flowered skirt. A pair of trousers might have

saved her from the worst, so that she might not have needed Luke's reluctant administrations.

Swallowing painfully, she regarded the crisp darkness of his downbent head. It was difficult to imagine him as the very young man he must have been when he had first brought a wife back to the islands. How long ago was it that the same boy had changed into a man with a granite-like immunity to all the tender emotions which must surely be possible between a man and woman? He had built a wall deliberately and a girl would only get hurt throwing herself against it. Over the years he had grown hard, forceful, as bleak as the sea when grey clouds were above it. He would not be likely to change now, not in his thirties. At this age a man's ways were set and the strength of Luke Harrison's personality would never condone a moment's weakness. Passion might not be ruled out, but tenderness would never be allowed.

Taking her silence for a very satisfactory subjugation, Luke relented a little, his eyes lifting as he straightened, to swiftly examine her face to which the colour was slowly returning. 'Your leg shouldn't hurt now, but you'd probably be wiser to use it as little as possible this morning. You don't have to fight me every inch of the way, you know. It will make little difference in the long run.'

'It might!'

She spoke so low he could scarcely have heard what she said, but his brief, ironic laughter proclaimed that he had. 'Time will convince you,' he assured her emphatically, 'that we don't always have to be at each other's throats. Life will be pleasanter, my small Tanya, when you learn to please me rather than fling insults.'

'And you intend I should sit here alone, repenting of my sins,' she exclaimed, trying to close her mind to the implications of what he was saying.

He looked half amused, half intolerant. 'You don't have to do anything of the sort. Send for Toma to fetch your hat and you can come with me around the plantation. I think some fresh air might help you get things in better perspective. All islands are individual even if they look the same. It applies to men, too, though it might take you longer to realise it. Now run along and fetch that hat. If you're good I promise you another cup of coffee down at the office.'

CHAPTER FOUR

WHILE Tanya would like to have refused, if only because it was Luke's suggestion, she decided, after a moment's obvious hesitation, that she would be a fool to miss such an opportunity. Wasn't it what she had been seeking, a means of satisfying a growing interest and curiosity? This way she might achieve this without Luke guessing, by pretending she felt forced to fall in with his wishes. She didn't doubt that the olive branch he held out did anything but conceal temporarily his usual domineering self.

While she waited as he issued brief orders to Toma, she reflected uncertainly. Luke could hurt. Mysteriously he had rendered her curiously vulnerable to his threats. He could make her instantly afraid, his tongue able to whip up almost as much torment as his hands. Her position here was subservient. She was someone to care for his old nanny of whom he was clearly very fond, and he didn't want to bring in a stranger who might pester him for attentions he was not prepared to give. This morning he looked so tall and handsome in his bush shirt and shorts that Tanya turned her eyes away. Dressed this way he had an air of hard ruthlessness about him and she could see he might have a point in declaring that women chased after him. Not that these had been his exact words, but it had been what he meant, and, in the face of them, Tanya wasn't sure if he considered her an enemy or friend. Possibly she was being as egotistical as he in imagining he ever really thought of her at all.

Her hat firmly on her small head, she followed him outdoors. In the freshness of early morning the lagoon looked softly silken, gleaming in the sunlight, the white foam of every turning wave sparkling like crystal. With wistful longing Tanya gazed at it, missing her swim which had become as ritual as awakening. All around the year she had swum since coming to the Pacific, and learnt to love the warm, translucent buoyancy of the deep waters. But it was a perfect morning and, in spite of the sadness that still lay in her heart, she felt her spirits rising. There was much here she was going to miss and if every hour was to be a sort of bonus then she must make the most of the time she had left. Yet much as she loved living in the South Pacific it mustn't lessen her resolution to leave. Nor must she become so indebted to Luke as to make this impossible.

The smell of the sea, sharp and salty, mingled with that of the land with its tropical plants and vegetation, the ever-lasting smell of the coconut. The smell of copra could pervade everything, but it was something one got used to and scarcely noticed. Out here the air was initially clean and pleasant and there were other things wafted on the air besides coconut. There could be tantalising whiffs of sandalwood and cinnamon, raw black pepper and saffron —herbs of every kind, flowers of every kind, too. These grew in such wild profusion that eventually one took them for granted, but their scent was always there, touching the nostrils, stirring the senses, making one aware of a kind of paradise not easily found elsewhere. It was a good land, a good place to live in. In spite of some drawbacks, Tanya knew she could never be in two minds about that.

Luke slanted her a sideways glance as if he guessed her thoughts as she paused to breathe deeply and wanted only to emphasise them. 'Here one can get very near to heaven, wouldn't you agree?'

She had to be contrary, if only in self-defence. 'One could tire of it.'

He thrust her sardonically into the waiting jeep. 'I'd be willing to wager you don't. Is it a surfeit of the good things in life or the senses you're afraid of?'

'You only see what you want to see,' she retorted coolly, knowing the latter applied but doing her best to hide it from him.

He released the brake as the engine sprang to life. 'I've

never found it difficult to spot the obvious.'

Her too sensitive pulse missed a beat. 'In my case what is it that stands out a mile?'

'That you might be tailor-made for what I have in mind.' His mouth twisted sarcastically at the way she challenged him.

She smiled without much humour as they bumped uncomfortably between the rows of palms. 'You talk as though I were a piece of pliable material!'

'Unfortunately people are not that,' Luke grunted, steadying the wheel, the muscles of his powerful forearms coping easily as the vehicle lurched. 'With you I have the unexpected ingredient of spice which ensures, when you're around, that life will never be dull.'

Depending which way one looked at it, his last remark could be alarming. Tanya felt frankly uneasy. 'We only discussed a week or two. I didn't agree to stay voluntarily —or indefinitely!'

Coolly he took no notice of her heated protestations. 'I'm not interested in what you imagine you agreed to. Neither am I prepared to argue with you. You're too keen to jump to all the wrong conclusions. Early mornings should be for other things besides words. Certainly not for dissension!'

If his face had possessed even an ounce of tenderness she might not have known such a continuing desire to oppose him. He was condescending, his meaning so clear she didn't, this time, have to ask for an explanation. She had lived on the islands long enough to realise the born islander was a very sensuous creature. Did Luke Harrison imagine she was, too? The girls, in their lighthearted fashion, had been fond of startling her young ears with stories of their various love affairs, but while it had seemed only polite to listen she hadn't necessarily adopted their rather licentious ways.

Yet the native girls could make such matters sound completely natural and Tanya had often found herself wondering with a half ashamed curiosity if she was missing something. She had discovered, anyway, that her innocence was not something for self-congratulation. This didn't stop her from exclaiming to Luke, 'You seem to think I'd do well to be as imprudent as the islanders?'

'Not all of them,' he grinned, not pretending to misunderstand, 'but don't underrate your own possibilities. These people are earthy but innocent. They have their faith and beliefs the same as you and I, only they're not quite so inhibited.'

'I've learnt that much!' Tanya rejoined with conviction, her cheeks flushing, 'but I still don't share all their views.'

'A pity,' he drawled laconically, 'as they're without stiff pride and resentment and have learnt to accept what comes their way.'

She shot him an indignant glance which he didn't appear to notice. He might find, too, that she wasn't so easily subdued, and that love for her was an essential factor before she gave herself to any man. But she had never been in love yet. No doubt he had little use for an inexperienced virgin.

His quick exclamation broke through her wavering thoughts. They had reached a part of the plantation where weeds were growing thick. 'They grow so damn quickly,' he groaned.

'Does it matter?' she queried, bewildered, not at all up on the cultivation of the coconut.

'Naturally it matters,' he said impatiently. 'If the weeds grow too high the workers can't find the ripe nuts when they fall. That these weeds have grown so high points to neglect.'

'I see,' she murmured, for once not minding his shortness. She knew, in spite of the general image of South Seas indolence, that most planters led extremely busy lives.

Luke relented with a slight smile as he caught her uncertain expression. 'I expect you've only seen the wild coconut palm?'

Eagerly she nodded. 'The natives set great store by it. On Karowi they seemed to use everything about it—the wood to build their homes and for fires, the bark, roots, milk and oil for various other purposes.'

'You don't have to tell me all this,' he teased.

'What I mean is you only use it for commercial purposes.'

He drove on, his eyes amused, ignoring her rebuke. 'Without the properly planted commercial plantation many of the islanders wouldn't find a proper livelihood. Many of the coconut palms on this island are well over seventy years old and still produce nuts. A palm must be about six or seven years old before it starts bearing and each nut takes several years to grow to full size and ripen.'

Glad to get away from personalities, if only for a few minutes, she commented curiously, 'I've noticed coconuts of varying sizes on the same palm.'

'Nuts drop all the year round,' he said, 'usually at night, mostly from June to September. On an average only one or two a week, but one never knows when. It certainly doesn't pay to loiter under the palms.'

She smiled. 'So you're especially busy just now?'

'Too busy to welcome any complications back at the house, Tanya. To waste time where it can be avoided. This is where you're being quite useful.'

He drove swiftly on, as if deliberately over the uneven route, giving her no chance to answer. The roughness of the terrain took her breath away, forcing her to hang on to her seat to avoid being thrown about and bruised. It grew hotter, but this she didn't mind, being well used to it. She even revelled in it, but couldn't help feeling resentful that, after his appreciative words—if this was what they had been—Luke appeared to have no proper regard for her safety. He had asked her to accompany him, but it was clear he didn't intend cosseting her.

A little further and he slammed on the brakes again. Where a group of island workers had gathered nuts into piles and, after slitting each one with an axe, were neatly scooping out the white kernel with a knife.

'At one time,' he told her briefly, 'the oil was shipped

out in casks. Now most of the coconut kernel is dried and sent out as copra. We use kilns for drying the kernel. It produces better copra than the old method of drying out in the sun, which you've probably seen.'

On the island where Tanya had lived the natives had let the trees grow where nature had intended, but here she noticed the rows were neatly spaced out. Luke informed her, when she asked, that there were about fifty palms to the acre with the heavier crop near to the sea.

'How much of the island do you own?' She stared about her curiously, aware that he might think her impertinent but realising the importance of knowing if there were any other planters. To find this out she must risk his wrath.

'The whole of it.'

'All of it!' she repeated stupidly, the knowledge alarming her so that dismay flashed too obviously across her expressive face.

'So you thought to seek asylum,' he taunted. 'A long time ago my great-grandparents enjoyed their privacy and land was cheap, if not too profitable. If you can manage it our nearest neighbour might be quite accommodating and is not too far away.'

She thought it wiser not to deny what he said, and stared at him defiantly, 'I might feel like a change of company.' She presumed this neighbour lived on another island.

'You've scarcely tried mine yet.'

The dryness of his tone was intimidating, but she refused to give in. 'You're forgetting ours is just a business arrangement, Mr Harrison. We don't relax much in each other's company. Besides, you're busy.'

He met her stubborn gaze head on, his coldly calculating. 'The evenings can be very pleasant, Tanya, and I'm sure I can spare you a little time. I promise you'll soon learn to relax, if you think this is so necessary.'

'One has to like a person first!'

'I'll try to guarantee this as well, my dear.'

'Some time,' she persisted, a small devil driving her,

'I should like to meet this neighbour.'

'Don't try.' His voice came softly but sliced into her like steel. Tanya visibly started and Luke's foot pressed the accelerator so roughly that she was thrown back sharply against him, the impact of his hard chest drawing the breath from her body. 'Sorry,' he apologised formally, but she could detect no remorse in his tones.

She straightened, not daring to trust herself to speak, and saw they had arrived at some large, tin-roofed copra sheds where the dried coconut waited to be shipped out to be manufactured into soap and margarine and various other products. A village lay beside the sheds, many of the islanders' homes oval-shaped with thatched roofs. Other than these there was only a small church and two bungalows which housed the offices and Luke's French overseer along with other European workers.

The islanders who were around stared at her, but she wasn't disturbed by their interest which she knew from experience was always polite. She guessed they knew a great deal more about her than their smiling faces betrayed. These were a people she liked and had felt honoured to live among. When a young wife brought her baby for Tanya to see she smiled warmly and agreed to hold it eagerly when the girl held it out, although she didn't understand what they were saying. So many languages were spoken on the islands, it would be almost impossible to learn each one.

They laughed now, their dark eyes happy with approval as Tanya hugged the beautiful little baby to her. Its mother could not have been much older than seventeen, but already she seemed to have assumed the role of a settled housewife and mother. They spoke to Luke, tentatively at first, then with a gathering confidence as he smiled.

'Don't you want to know what they're saying?' he jibed dryly, his eyes gleaming wickedly as she flushed.

She was quite aware that the flowing tide of their remarks had to do with Luke and herself, and she guessed the

nature of them by the way their eyes roamed her slight
figure. 'If you're trying to embarrass me you must think of
something else. These people only see women as potential
mothers!' The smile left her face as an odd tremor shook
her when her eyes inadvertently met his and with a hasty
movement she gave the child back to its mother.

Luke sobered strangely, too, and turned to address one
of the older men on what appeared to be a specific problem. While he did so, Tanya controlled herself and squat-
ted back on her heels to watch the other children, fascinated
as always by the way they munched through quantities of
oranges and bananas, mandarins and fresh pineapples. Fruit
was there for the picking and seemed to form a staple part
of their diet which in some cases might only be supple-
mented by meat on special occasions. There was plenty of
fish, however, so they did get some variety.

Luke said, as they walked towards the bungalows, 'I
shouldn't have thought a girl like you would be so taken
with children.'

So he had noticed. 'Why shouldn't I be?' She bent her
tawny head, yet went on bravely, 'I might have some of my
own one day.'

'You wouldn't find them a nuisance?' His voice was
mildly indifferent, as if neither the question or her answer
was of any real consequence, but his glance, which she
didn't see, was keen and hard.

'Of course not!' she retorted indignantly, then remembered, too late, what Miss Logan had said about Luke's
wife not wanting a family. Miss Logan could have been
wrong. Anyway, it was not for Luke to judge all women
alike. Thousands of women adored their families, and
having them. 'I've always loved the island children,' she
went on, striving to change the subject to one which
bothered her less. 'Perhaps, one day, I might write a book
about them. I've actually made copious notes.'

The lines on his hard, handsome face seemed to ease
with a kind of remote satisfaction, but he merely said
lightly, 'It could be an interesting hobby.'

'I shall want it to be more than a hobby,' she answered sharply.

'Really?' His voice was degrees cooler. 'I'm afraid career women bore me.'

'Because you don't meet many here, or that the set you move in doesn't include women who must work for their living?' she taunted, suspecting he spoke with the deliberate intention of annoying her because something in her answer hadn't pleased him.

'I look to women to entertain me, not tell me how to do my job,' he returned impassively.

Tanya sighed, regretting such arrogance. 'Unfortunately I shall have to keep myself. Perhaps not by writing, but I must certainly work.'

'Not here you don't. You might for a little amusement, but nothing else. I have other plans for you.'

'I'm sure you have plans for everyone!' She tried to pull away from the biting fingers which caught her arm. 'You make a fortune out of copra and think money gives you a right to dictate as you wish!'

'Calm down,' he ground out, giving her a slight shake, not caring apparently that anyone watching might see. 'You might be right about my having to dictate . . .'

'That wasn't the way I put it!'

'I realise your meaning wasn't so charitable, but it's difficult to be two different persons. My workers look for decisiveness, a strong guiding hand. If I didn't have it I wouldn't last—neither would they, for that matter. As for my profits, I don't have anything to complain of at present, nor am I apprehensive about the immediate future, but my father could have told you about the 1930s, when prices dropped so low the nuts weren't worth harvesting. Many planters went broke. We didn't, we held out and it paid off, but at a very high personal cost.'

Tanya was silent. She didn't doubt that what he told her was true, but she didn't want to get involved in his family's misfortunes, if this was what he referred to. Never would it do to feel compassion for Luke Harrison, to let him get under her skin. She might finish up drooling over him, as probably did other misguided women. Tui had sometimes reminisced about the bad times and suddenly she wished passionately that her father hadn't chosen to live like a hermit, that he had been willing to be more involved with the islands generally. Only now was she really beginning to realise how cut off she had been, how isolated from the worst aspects as well as the good. Although if the worst aspect was to be the man beside her then her father might have been wise in trying to protect her.

Luke's overseer was a man, like Luke, in his thirties. Tanya thought he might be younger. He had been born on the island of French parents, and did not want to leave. While talking to him Luke kept a proprietorial hand on Tanya's arm. He might well have put a brand on her, she thought bitterly, knowing the futility of trying to escape him. It didn't seem likely that Jules would make an obliging accomplice, should she ever need one. He was too obviously under Luke's thumb and would never do anything to jeopardise his position here. The glances he slanted occasionally at Tanya were interested but cool.

It was lunch time before they returned to the house. Afterwards Luke left again for the plantations and Tanya resumed the not too difficult task of watching over Miss Logan. Miss Logan was so good all afternoon that Tanya began to feel Luke exaggerated her condition. True, she had acted rather foolishly a few nights previously, but since then she had behaved perfectly. She slept through the hotter part of the day in her room, then took iced drinks with Tanya on the veranda in the early evening.

'Luke will probably be late tonight,' she informed Tanya, as she rose to change for dinner. 'He's particularly busy just now, so we mustn't object.'

'No, of course not,' Tanya answered obligingly, not because she felt an answer necessary but Miss Logan always expected one. Tanya felt she wouldn't mind if he never returned, but she didn't speak her thoughts aloud, not being absolutely sure if they were true or not. It was frustrating that she didn't seem certain of anything any more when Luke was around, and that he could make her shiver even when he wasn't near!

Miss Logan always insisted on sleeping in the old nursery and Tanya left her at the door with Toma, the gentle Melanesian servant girl, who would help her to change. The girl took over from Tanya, who promised to collect Miss Logan later.

'Put something smart on for Luke,' Miss Logan ordered Tanya happily as she turned away. 'Luke likes his women soignée, dear. You'd do well to remember.'

Tanya couldn't follow Miss Logan's advice, dressing only to please a man, one in particular. She found she couldn't, with Miss Logan's words ringing so freshly in her ears, think of changing at all. Suddenly the walls of the house seemed to be closing in on her and while she tried to convince herself it was because she had become unused to living in one she knew she must seek a few minutes outside in the fresh air. Memories of wild, lonely beaches came to her strongly. When she closed her eyes she could see sands beaten white by the sea. Those sands, the lone sea and sky had been her constant companions for over two years. She had a crazy feeling she was neglecting them and that they might bring Thor, the Scandinavian god of thunder, down on her head. She had felt unsettled since she had come here and felt an almost sick longing to go and lose herself in the elements, that they might wash away the new torments that beset her. That she might find herself again in the deep caverns which were palaces of calm beneath stormy waters.

As Tanya stood silently contemplating the long white corridor, such was her desire to escape it could no longer be contained. She wasn't sure that Luke would approve, but as he wasn't here she couldn't consult him. Miss Logan surely wouldn't come to any harm and she wouldn't be gone long.

Afterwards she wondered why Luke should be so annoyed about a girl going for a swim. Maybe he had every right to be furious with her, but she hadn't seemed able to resist going down to the sea. Maybe she hadn't wanted to!

Taking a large towel as she couldn't find a handy swimsuit, she escaped while Dino was looking the other way. The night was warm, the lagoon like a millpond as she negotiated the bottom of the garden and slipped out of her clothes on the beach. The moon hadn't yet risen, but the stars were brilliant and cast a soft light. With a happier sigh she slid into the water which closed around her slim body as if it had been specially waiting for her.

She swam longer than she had intended, the darkness of the night holding no terrors for her. Turning on her back after a while, she floated dreamily, lazily watching the stars, feeling the tension draining from her. For the first time in days she stopped considering her present dilemma, relaxing instead and finding pleasure in allowing her mind to go completely blank. It was a trick she had often practised when her father had been particularly petulant and everything had seemed too much. There was only the softly lapping water, the cry of a lone night bird to break the velvety, soporific silence which she loved.

It was later than she thought as she left the sea and ran back up the beach. Water streamed from her long hair down her bare skin, but after one startled glance at her luminous watch she dried swiftly before putting on her clothes. She was in such a panic to get dressed and reach the house she didn't see anything until a voice exclaimed tightly, 'It seems my everlasting fate to find you running around like this—out in the dark when you should have been changing for dinner like any normal girl.'

Tanya gasped, her fright a small one but very real as she jerked around to stare up at Luke, uneasily aware of his close regard. Because his eyes glinted dangerously in the dim light, she said warily, 'I didn't think I was adding to my crimes by having a swim. I don't sleep well.'

'You've forgotten what it's like to sleep in a comfortable bed.'

If she had been indiscreet he didn't spare her. Maybe it was true, she hadn't slept on a proper mattress for a long time. The one on her bed in Luke's house was luxurious by comparison to the straw one she had had on the other island, yet she found it vaguely uncomfortable. 'You keep hinting that I lived like a savage,' she spluttered, bending to pull on her sneakers. One she couldn't find and she started groping around in the sand.

He sighed grimly, spotting it quicker than she did, passing it to her after picking it up. As his fingers touched hers she flinched visibly as their contact seared strangely. She heard the snap of his white teeth. 'If I did think you a little savage would I be so wrong? You must re-learn the advantages of a more civilised way of life.'

She noticed he didn't say anything about pleasure.

He continued, as she straightened beside him, 'I don't want you swimming in the dark by yourself. That's an order. If you must swim then ask me. I'll come with you.'

That would spoil everything. Her mind ignored her throbing pulse that argued otherwise. 'Sharks rarely come inside the reef,' she pointed out. 'I like swimming alone and no one can see me.'

'I'll admit you're too brown to make an easy target for the eyes,' he drawled, 'but others, like mine, are trained like cats. You swim without anything on.'

He might have been discussing the weather, yet she felt a warm tide of confusion sweep right over her. He must have seen, unless he was merely guessing.

She doubted no longer as his hand went out to draw her harshly to him, his voice roughening. 'Brown and damp and childishly curved, but how innocent, I wonder? Have you no sense in that shining head of yours, or do you deliberately put temptation in a man's way?'

She couldn't speak and made no attempt to pull herself away until he lowered his head and his lips came swiftly down on the leaping pulse in her throat, as though he sought to still it with the savageness of his onslaught. Struggling wildly, she tried to escape him, knowing instinctively that if she didn't immediately she might be lost. He was stronger by far than she was but he surely couldn't want a girl who showed herself clearly unwilling to respond. If he thought she had planned this intentionally then he would soon discover he was mistaken!

But he refused to let her go, even as she entreated him, the hardness of his grip on her shoulders silent evidence of deeper emotions held temporarily in check. 'Stop struggling against the inevitable,' he commanded thickly, taking no notice whatsoever of her apparent distress.

She started hitting him then, with small clenched fists, beating him fiercely until she came slowly to realise she wasn't fighting him so much as herself, the flame within her which he seemed so easily to ignite. Ignoring her attempts to evade him, he began kissing her mouth into submission, one arm around her trembling shoulders, the other possessively around her hips, moulding her tightly against his hard frame.

As they swayed, locked together in the starlight, her arms went up to encircle his neck and she knew a wild longing to be taken by him, crushed down and transported in pain and ecstasy to those regions of the senses which were as yet unknown to her. She knew an urgent, scarcely controllable desire to explore them with him, to cling to him madly until he consented to do as she silently beseeched.

Then suddenly she was free, a foot between them where before there hadn't been so much as a breath of air, and he was taunting sardonically, 'You're learning fast,'

She put a hand up to her burning, shaking mouth. 'Next time you can look elsewhere for amusement!'

'That's just one of the things I'm looking for,' he retorted, enigmatically. 'We have to remember Elizabeth will be waiting and I don't want her coming out here to look for you.'

'I've only to shower and dress.' Tanya tried to adopt his cool tones, but her throat was painfully tight.

'And dry this!' He was near again, his hand grasping a handful of hair and squeezing until painful tears touched her eyes and she flinched from him. If he saw her tears they merely seemed to add to his quirk of satisfaction. 'Just remember what I told you about coming down here alone after dark. You can forget the rest.'

'Have it your own way!' Her insolent rejoinder evolved from pain. Did he think she was going to remind him!

With a soft exclamation Luke yanked her cruelly to him. 'One thing I won't tolerate is cheek!' He ran an abrasive finger across her bruised lips. 'Your mouth has a salty sweetness, but I hope you have the sense to realise your position here is not that of an honoured guest.'

'More like a prisoner! Certainly I couldn't consider myself honoured in any way by the way you choose to treat me!'

'Nor do you look on yourself as a serf, but then I like a little spirit.'

Abruptly he let her go again and she stared after his broad back as he turned indifferently away, wishing he was not so big and invulnerable. There were moments when she would have given anything to be able to reduce him in size, so she might crush him beneath her foot!

He thrust her indoors, not noticeably gentle, as if beneath his coolness his feelings might be as disturbed as hers. 'Down again,' he said, 'in ten minutes. Otherwise we'll start without you! And wear something blue.'

This seemed to set the pattern of the next weeks, Luke giving the orders and Tanya obeying them, feeling blindly that her feet were fixed helplessly on a course of ultimate disaster, but there was nothing she could do about it. It wasn't that he kept her a prisoner. He allowed her to wander within limits, he even took her around himself, and she would be free to go when Miss Logan left. It was the intervening days and evenings which disturbed Tanya. Luke Harrison was an extremly attractive man with a kind of polished vitality she found increasingly difficult to resist. If he purposefully set out to charm her she had little real doubt he would succeed, and she wanted desperately to leave with her heart intact as well as everything else.

The stupidity of her own response, the startling wantonness of her feelings when Luke had kissed her on the beach that evening was something she wanted to forget. That he had not attempted to kiss her again seemed to prove he had lost interest, which strengthened Tanya's resolve to put it from her own mind too.

For the most part of each day she looked after Miss Logan and during the hours Miss Logan rested after lunch she explored, wishing to familiarise herself with as much of Luke's island as possible. It became important, somehow, that she didn't rely wholly on his rather vague assurance that after Miss Logan went he would consider getting Tanya back to England. Each time she turned the conversation in this direction he adroitly changed it, and so skilfully that she didn't realise until afterwards that he always managed to avoid a downright commitment.

It didn't help that, much as she tried to avoid it, they still fought each other. Usually it was she who sparked off a disagreement, Luke who dismissed it with a few sharply chosen words that could occasionally cause her to tremble. At times she could feel a leashed violence in him, as if he were torn two ways over his treatment of her. He was busy on the plantation, and while this might explain why he hadn't left the island since she had arrived it did make her wonder. He was divorced, free to seek the company of other women, and there was an awareness about him sometimes when he glanced at her which made her quiver. He was not, she suspected, a man naturally inclined towards living like a hermit, and if such a thought secretly excited her it also made her wary. It would be utterly foolish to fall in love with him, dislike must be much easier to live with.

Yet more and more Tanya felt curious about his wife, until it became a kind of torment. She felt a growing desire to see what Rowena looked like. Nor did she feel altogether satisfied after worming it out of Miss Logan that Rowena was blonde. A blonde could be plain or beautiful, or something in between. She might be fat or thin or, again, nicely slender. Tanya, finding herself strangely obsessed by the looks of a woman she had little chance of meeting, asked Miss Logan casually, one day, if she had such a thing as a photograph.

Miss Logan shook her grey head, but appeared to think there was nothing unusual in Tanya's request. 'I'm sorry, dear. She didn't care for me, so I don't suppose she would have given me one if I'd asked for it. She did like her photograph taken, though, so I expect Luke must have lots tucked away somewhere, unless he's burnt them, and I doubt, somehow, if he'd do that. It's often the next best thing to having someone, isn't it? To be able to look at their snapshot.'

'Why should Luke want to look at a woman who left him?' Tanya asked, feeling the first stirrings of active antagonism within her.

'I'm not sure, dear,' Miss Logan sighed. 'She was very lovely.'

One morning Luke said at breakfast, 'I promised Elizabeth I would take her around the island and to her favourite beach before she leaves. We can have lunch there. I'll be back in a couple of hours. You can arrange a hamper with Dino and have Elizabeth ready.'

He was a strange man, Tanya mused, as she ran upstairs after agreeing with what the hamper should contain with Dino. Luke could be so ruthlessly hard when it suited him, yet here he was, willing to please his old nanny by escorting her on a picnic, an outing that would surely have little appeal to a man like him.

Miss Logan waited below, as excited as a schoolgirl and, just like a schoolgirl, promising to be good while Tanya collected her things. Tanya couldn't help feeling rather excited herself as she thrust a swimsuit which she had found into a bag with a towel and zipped herself into shorts and a brief top. Her hair she brushed quickly and tied behind her nape before jamming on a wide-brimmed hat. Her outfit didn't look too fashionable, but then it wasn't going to be that kind of day!

Luke drove carefully with Elizabeth sitting happily beside him. Tanya felt a moment's indignation when she considered the way he drove her, but she supposed she was young enough to put up with the bumps and bruises. Luke usually forgot she was there when he took her out. If she complained he might never ask her again, so she usually stayed silent. She sat behind the two in front, constrained yet eager, the morning sunlight catching the pure planes of her face, tilting the corners of her warmly curved mouth. Once when she caught Luke's narrowed gaze upon her in the driving mirror she coloured and averted her own eyes from his strongly modelled head, unaware until that moment that she had been staring.

The air was hot, but a breeze from off-shore kept the temperatures reasonable. They threaded their way slowly over many miles of the island, some of which Tanya hadn't seen before but with which Miss Logan was obviously familiar. Her old eyes sparkled and shone and it was quite apparent she was enjoying her outing. Talking to Luke and throwing the odd remark back to Tanya, one would have had to be extremely insensitive not to realise how much Miss Logan loved everything about her. How can she bear to leave it? Tanya wondered, scarcely conscious of the poignancy of her unspoken query.

The beach, when they reached Miss Logan's favourite cove, was soft and warm, the sea sparkling in deep blues and greens beneath the sun at the height of the day. Immediately Tanya jumped down, running quickly around to help Miss Logan from the truck while Luke spread rugs under the nearest breadfruit tree. Tanya was surprised that, despite the roughness and heat of their journey, Miss Logan looked almost as neat and cool as when they had started out. Ignoring Luke's advice to sit and rest a while, the old lady wandered down to the shore, quickly pouncing and exclaiming over various shells before Tanya could stop her.

'Come on, my small Hercules,' Luke teased, as Tanya bent and began gathering up some particularly beautiful specimens Miss Logan pointed to. He came up behind her, tossing her towel and swimsuit across her shoulders. 'You don't have to work all the time, you know. If I'm to enjoy myself you'd better begin concentrating on me. Otherwise I might refuse to come again.'

CHAPTER FIVE

CHANGING modestly into her swimsuit behind some bushes of white hibiscus, Tanya wondered how Luke could swing so quickly from one mood to another. This afternoon he was sardonically casual, tomorrow, or maybe in an hour's time, he would be grimly watchful, capable of making her heart shake with a nameless dread.

Now, as she emerged from her changing place, slender and beautiful, her hair swinging with a glossy heaviness about her shoulders, he continued to tease lightly and she decided to make the most of it. 'I noticed you found a swimsuit,' his green eyes glinted. 'I thought you said there wasn't one?'

'I found this in the bottom of a chest of drawers. I didn't actually look again until yesterday.'

'Why haven't you gone swimming again?'

Couldn't he simply glance at her and look away again? Did he have to assess her every curve, even if such a detached interest removed anything remotely personal from his gaze? 'I haven't had much time,' she hedged, hating the faint colour which crept beneath her skin as it became obvious he didn't believe her.

'Liar,' he exclaimed softly, yet the threat in his voice was gentle and he took her hand, as if disinclined to argue any further. 'It's a lovely day,' he added, as if by way of explanation. 'Elizabeth will take no harm for an hour. If you've missed your daily dip because of me we must make up for it.'

He passed her a pair of flippers and water-tight goggles and they swam in the crystal clear waters of the lagoon. If he guessed she hadn't risked swimming for fear of encountering him he said nothing more, and he could only guess if she didn't openly admit it. Feeling irrationally protected by her own deviousness, Tanya allowed herself to relax, to meander sublimely through the shoals of gaily coloured fish which darted carelessly around them. The warmth and buoyancy of the water, the gentle playfulness of the glistening, white-topped waves always made her feel good. Sometimes waves forty feet high dashed the reefs and she had seen islanders surfing them. She could surf fairly well herself, but tackled something less ambitious. The islanders, especially in a storm, could lose all sense of caution and once she had seen some of them drown. The memory of it could still make her shudder.

Today, Luke seemed determined she shouldn't dwell on anything so morbid. He took her beneath the water, guiding her to secret spots, pools of turquoise, azure, cobalt and emerald, every colour she could think of, all of them fascinating. Tanya, who after two years had learnt to spear a fish like a native, swam with all the fluid grace of the fish she had been compelled to seek out to supplement her father's meagre diet. While fully aware of the dangers surrounding the reefs she adored the wonders to be found in the coral caves below them, and today, with Luke by her side, his powerful body ready to shield her from any harm and restrain her more reckless inclinations, she enjoyed herself to the full.

When, eventually, he firmly dragged her out she wanted to protest, but finished up by merely staring at him meekly as he removed her mask with his own. The nearness of him with the water dripping from his broad, brown shoulders and the clustered dark hair on his chest did odd things to her breathing.

'I think Elizabeth has lunch ready,' he told her, mistaking her visible shudder for cold and wrapping a towel closely around her. 'You've been in long enough, anyway.'

Tanya, removing her eyes from him with effort, clutched the towel about her wet person and glanced to where Miss Logan waited patiently, a snowy white cloth already spread beneath the breadfruit tree, and a wave of guilt swept her. This was, after all, Miss Logan's day and while she had swum heedlessly Miss Logan had arranged their meal.

'I'm sorry,' she flushed, biting her full lower lip unhappily. 'I forgot my position.'

Just for a moment a kind of impatience darkened Luke's
features as he looked down on her. 'Don't worry, I'll remind you when you overstep the mark.' He strode back to
Miss Logan, pushing Tanya before him as if her apparent
bitterness annoyed him. 'You don't have to pretend you
have a conscience all of a sudden. Elizabeth means nothing
to you, you can't wait to get away.'

'I do—I mean I do like her. It's only you I want to leave!'

'Really?' His grin was cool, scarcely touching his hard
mouth. 'Then I'd better set about changing your mind,' he
jeered, his softer mood obviously fading.

Tanya, surprised to find she was still hungry after this,
flopped nervously beside Miss Logan, grateful for the
coffee that was thrust quickly into her shaking hands. How
had Miss Logan guessed she felt suddenly cold all over?

Luke took a bottle of wine from its iced container and
filled glasses which Tanya privately thought too expensive
for an outing such as this. Wistfully she compared them
with the paper cups she had taken on picnics in England.
Luke made her put down her coffee cup and take one. 'This
might help you count your blessings more easily!'

'I won't transgress again,' she assured him mutinously,
her small face, washed clean of make-up, startling in its
purity.

'Then stop making an issue out of something which
doesn't exist,' he advised harshly, and she dared not ask
him what he meant. Not without risking that last bit of
harmony—if it was still there.

After lunch, shaded by the tree above her and replete
with wine and good food, Miss Logan slept in her low
canvas chair with its protective canopy. She even began to
snore gently.

With a wry shrug Luke picked up a rug, removing it and
Tanya twenty yards away. 'I can't stand women who do
that,' he grinned. 'I hope you don't, Tanya. I might forgive
you anything but that.'

Her senses reeling, she dropped weakly to the rug. 'My mannerisms will never be your concern!' She looked back at Miss Logan, urgently needing to change the subject. 'I think I should sit by her.'

'I can see her from here,' he promised grimly. 'Under the circumstances I'm sure she'd rather be alone.'

She knew what he meant, so subsided to an uneasy silence, conscious that he had dropped down beside her. He lay on his back, his hands behind his head, his eyes mercifully closed.

'Tired?' he asked suddenly, just when she thought he had succumbed like Miss Logan. Because she was, she denied it quickly, holding herself stiffly in case she touched him.

'Bored, then?' His voice was degrees colder. 'Women must have continual excitement or they're fed-up. Above everything they hate being tied down.'

'Luke—I . . .'

'Don't bother to deny it.' Cynically he turned to look at her again. 'How did you offset the boredom you must have experienced on your small island, Tanya? Did you have nocturnal visitors I didn't hear about?'

She tried to stay cool. 'You know if that was true your bush telegraph would have informed you.'

'Not necessarily. Your small brigade of islanders proved very loyal. When a woman sets out to charm she usually makes a good job of it. They always spoke most highly of the little white missy.'

Luke's wife seemed to have left him with a rare opinion of women! Unless he had already had it before she had married him and she had left him because she had been unable to stand it? 'If I thought I had charm don't you think I would have tried it on you?' Tanya cried jeeringly.

'You wouldn't know how,' his tone was insolent, 'you're too green. The soft little glances between fluttering lashes were in short supply when you were manufactured.'

Her face flushed scarlet, but she said bravely, 'I'm not all that naïve. I did have a job for a short time, although I wasn't fully trained. I saw quite a bit of life.'

'The seamy side?'

'That's the only side men like you remember!'

'You can say that again,' his voice mocked. 'Every bad little bitch I remember!'

Tanya was so shocked she felt momentarily helpless and because her eyes filled with unpredictable tears she closed them tightly, burying her face in her hands, a sense of inescapable disaster settling on her. The hard cutting edge to his voice suggested, as it often did, that he had set out deliberately to upset her, but she couldn't ignore the underlying contempt in his words. Quite obviously his opinion of women included herself.

She couldn't remember falling asleep, and it was with sheer horror that she woke up later to find herself snuggled cosily against him instead of frozen to her former side of the rug. Her head lay on his outstretched arm and, to make matters worse, one of her own arms was flung across his wide chest.

'Luke!' Dismay made her voice hoarse, but she managed a whisper, which was curiously ineffectual. When she lifted her head her eyes were within inches of his and he was staring unblinking at her. Swiftly she dropped her stunned gaze, her heart pounding.

'What is it?' He made no effort to let her go and when she began to pull frantically away, his free hand went to her narrow waist, holding her to him.

She had to apologise for curling up to him like this, but she seemed transfixed, her eyes lifting again to his as the blood whipped through her veins, betraying the wild upheaval within her.

'You've been sleeping, Tanya,' he teased softly. He spoke gently as though to reassure her, but his gaze was keen on her bemused face. 'I liked the way you clung to me, but I'm not making mountains out of molehills. Neither, I hope, are you.'

'No.'

His voice was pitched low. 'I like having you in my

arms. You grow on a man, Tanya, but you're much too young for me—if not in years, in experience.'

'There was a bigger age gap between my parents and they were happy.'

'You're not proposing to me, by any chance?'

Realising it could have sounded like this, she flushed scarlet. 'I wasn't even thinking of such a thing,' she said defensively.

'I see.' The hand on her shoulder slid to tug a heavy swathe of hair from off her slender neck and she felt he was laughing at her.

Again she tried to wriggle discreetly from the imprisoning grip on her waist while trying to resist the waves of desire which were suddenly hitting her. It became a kind of torment, leaving her strangely speechless, and when she didn't succeed in releasing herself, rather than actively fight him, she attempted to bury her betraying face against him again.

This time Luke laughed outright, but his laughter was dry as though she irritated as well as amused. His hand came under her chin, bringing her head up forcibly. 'Stop trying to evade me, Tanya, or yourself. Learn to please me and it will be much easier in the long run.'

Tanya couldn't find the breath to reply. She quivered in his hold when she ought to have been protesting wildly, conscious of the heat of his heavy body against her own. He might think her young, not to be taken seriously, but he was aware of her, she suspected, as a man is aware of a woman. He shifted abruptly on to his side, leaning above her, and Tanya, putting up her hands to push him away, came instantly in contact with his smooth flesh because of his unbuttoned shirt. Carelessly he had left it open and her hands curled convulsively as shock touched them like electric sparks. Then her tense fingers unclenched again, spreading over his warm, hair-roughened skin, feeling the thudding beat of his heart.

Suddenly his control seemed to snap. 'Why fight it, Tanya?' he asked harshly, pulling her strongly against him while his mouth sought her creamy neck and his hands moved with firm, caressing movements over her narrow hips. 'Think of this as an experiment if you like, but don't try to avoid me.'

She tried to, but the whole world seemed to be spinning away from her. He was too imperious, his will stronger than her own, making it an excuse to surrender to his superior strength with a soft little moan. Feverishly she crossed her arms behind his head, uncaring of anything before the sweeping depth of her insistent emotions and, curving her delicate jaw with ungentle fingers, his mouth found hers, parting her lips with the urgency of his desire.

There was no sound, no more struggle as she drowned in sensual sensation where nothing else mattered but that Luke should go on making love to her. The way he claimed her mouth and drained it brought a pleasure so intense as to be almost pain, but a pain she welcomed as it carried her towards realms of unexplored ecstasy. His tanned body crushed hers and she wanted his kisses, to be possessed by him.

But even as his hand sought and found the betraying swell of her breasts and his mouth followed, Miss Logan was standing near them, gazing towards them disapprovingly. Her precise tones fell on them coolly. 'My head occasionally plays tricks nowadays, but I think I know what I'm looking at!'

'Go away, Elizabeth!' Tanya, immediately aghast in his arms, heard Luke mutter threateningly.

There came a moment's awful silence during which she found it impossible to return completely from the soaring heights to which he had taken her. He had unbuttoned her brief top as his searching hands had caressed her and her bare, slender legs were wedged firmly under his, almost preventing her from moving. All of which Miss Logan must see!

'She's very young,' Miss Logan obviously thought it her duty to point out.

'She's also very beautiful, Elizabeth, and I want her,'

Luke replied briefly, his eyes remorselessly on Tanya's trembling lips.

'Then you should ask her properly, not like this!'

'This way she doesn't have to make a choice, Elizabeth. Now would you kindly go away!'

Suddenly Tanya came to her senses, hating herself but disliking Luke more. With an unexpected twist of her trembling limbs she jerked free from his arms. 'Wait for me, Elizabeth,' she cried, as Miss Logan anxiously hesitated while taking a backwards step. 'Don't you see, he's only teasing both of us. What you saw meant nothing—nothing at all that you need worry about.' Tanya didn't look at Luke. 'Sometimes there's a devil in him.'

'It's nothing I don't know, child.' If Miss Logan looked relieved she was still anxious. 'I'd advise you to stay clear of him in some moods.'

'He probably only meant to be companionable,' Tanya faltered, making things worse, her conversation hurtling inanely along as if she couldn't help herself.

'Morals, here, can leave a lot to be desired.' Not easily fooled, Miss Logan spoke severely, her eyes on Tanya's hot face.

'Are you discussing Tanya's or mine?' Luke mocked, coming up behind them, the rug slung carelessly across his shoulder, his glance taunting as Tanya paled with near anger. 'You haven't any idea what Tanya is like.'

'Stop it, Luke,' Miss Logan spoke sharply, clearly feeling she must take charge of the situation. 'I know she's particularly innocent.'

'Then you know more than I do,' he responded coolly, helping Miss Logan into her seat and slamming the door. Of Tanya he took no more notice whatsoever and she could only conclude that he regretted some of the afternoon's events almost as much as she did.

Luke dined out that evening, so she ate dinner alone with Miss Logan, who insisted that Tanya continue to call her Elizabeth. Tanya, who thought Miss Logan wouldn't have noticed that she had accidentally called her that on the

beach, apologised and said it wasn't necessary. Miss Logan
replied that it was and that she had been going to ask
Tanya to do so for the last week, so Tanya nodded, in a
slightly bewildered fashion, and agreed. If she hadn't
known better she might have suspected Miss Logan, for
some reason or other, was doing her best to put her at ease.

Miss Logan, as if nothing untoward had occurred to spoil
her picnic, discussed her new shells and how much she
had enjoyed her outing. She did not mention Luke at all.
Tanya would loved to have known where he went, but
could not bring herself to ask. Possibly he had dinner with
his overseer occasionally, a sort of working arrangement as
they were so very busy just now during the day. And today
Luke had taken a holiday, which must mean he had things
to catch up on. Wouldn't it have been easier to ask his
manager to come to the house?

Tanya frowned slightly, only half listening as Miss
Logan chattered. Miss Logan would know very well what
Luke was doing. Surely it was unnatural of her not to
mention it? It struck Tanya suddenly and coldly that he
might be seeing a girl, someone she knew nothing about.
Recalling the savageness of one or two of his remarks when
he had bumped into her on the stairs on his way out,
she shuddered afresh. He had practically accused her of
enjoying herself on the beach at his expense, but that he
could go straight from her arms to those of another was
painfully humiliating—or would have been if the hurt
hadn't affected her heart more than pride.

All through the night she lay, mysteriously unable to
sleep in spite of a busy day behind her. She imagined she
heard Luke come home in the early hours, but couldn't
be sure, and uncertainty filled her with an aching alarm.
Each time the old house creaked and whispered in the trade
winds her softly vulnerable mouth trembled.

The desire she knew to know what his wife actually
looked like grew until it seemed she could think of nothing else. Eventually, impatient to put an end to her own
foolish curiosity, she vowed she would look in the library

at the first opportunity to see if she could find a photograph.

She got no chance, however, until one afternoon, two days later, when Miss Logan was resting and Luke went out. When he told her he might be delayed in getting back that evening she assured him it didn't matter.

'Isn't it time things began to matter to you again?' he jeered cruelly. 'Almost six weeks since your father died. You should be starting to put it behind you.'

For a moment Tanya clenched her hands tight, seeing only arrogance in his expression. She gazed straight in front, trying not to be so overwhelmingly conscious of his eyes, aware that they had slipped from her profile down her smooth, slender neck which the open top of her blouse left bare. Wasn't it madness, with his glance so ironic, to remember what it was like in his arms? 'You have to twist everything I say. I wasn't even thinking of my father. Not then,' she added hastily, not willing to give the impression she never did—not even to please Luke.

'So it's only myself you don't mind if you never see again?'

'No. That is, I don't really see what our relationship, good or otherwise, has to do with it. You—you know I can't remain here indefinitely. Nor would you want me to.'

'How would you know what I wanted?' he smiled curtly, derisively. 'One of these days, when we're somewhere where Elizabeth can't possibly save you, we'll have a talk, you and I. A proper one, so you'd better be prepared. I don't have unlimited patience with evasiveness, girls who lead a man on and then haven't the courage to see something they started through to the end.'

Tanya watched his broad back disappear indifferently through the door, heard the rev of an engine, unnecessarily loud as if the foot controlling it was touched with violence, and she shivered at the coldness that encircled her heart as the noise faded in the distance. It was madness—she ran both hands over her hot face as if to rub out every remembered feature of him. Wasn't it crazy to feel in her bones that she was falling in love with a man who would never want her? Not permanently, not as his wife. Her senses swam with remembered sensations, the lingering pressure of Luke's mouth, his hand raking through her tawny hair, his face smothered in the silken texture and scent of it. The way in which he had locked her to him and kissed her, deliberately, savagely, until the whole of her had ached to respond in every way.

What could she do? Desperately she walked blindly into the library and closed the door, leaning back on the hard, smooth wood of the door frame, pressing her face despairingly against it. How she wished she could be a child again and could run to her parents for comfort and advice. How many girls could so easily leave home and turn their backs on this wonderful source of compassion she did not know. She must go home—not that there was anyone there now who would want her, but she couldn't stay here. It would be unbearable to see Luke each day, fearing she loved him. He had kissed her and each time there had been mockery and desire but not love.

She waited until the heavy tortured tattoo of her heart died down to a leaden calm before walking apprehensively across the room. In England it was known, in larger houses, as the library, but here the thick curtains and carpet of its English counterpart would have been out of place. Here there was a cool, tiled floor, spread with light rugs, and windows across which mosquito nets were discreetly draped. There was no desk but low marble and glass-topped tables, comfortable chairs and, above the low cupboards encircling the walls, a plentiful supply of books.

Tanya's eyes fixed magnetically on the cupboards, ignoring the old prints and mounted maps which at any other time she would have found fascinating. Those cupboards must surely hold such things as photographs and her encounter with Luke only seemed to strengthen her desire to find them.

She hadn't thought it would be so easy. Behind a large box, which looked as if it might hold jewellery or something valuable, she found a pile of albums. They looked dusty and neglected, but Rowena's photograph must surely be between some of the pages. Quickly Tanya pulled out the box which burst open as it fell with a crash to the floor, revealing its contents. Tanya didn't so much as glance at it. Her feverish eyes were concentrated on the albums, her fingers fumbling almost clumsily through the greenish pages, but she could find no one who looked like her mental picture of Luke's wife. She spent long moments poring over snaps of Luke and his parents and brother, obviously taken years ago, There were many pictures of islanders and parts of the island, what might amount to almost a photographic history of a plantation, but none of Luke and a girl. Not one of Luke and the girl he had loved enough to make his wife.

Her heart dull with disappointment, she closed the last album and began putting them back, trying to calm the still tortuous need within her to see what Rowena was like. As she struggled to replace everything neatly in their former positions, so no one would guess they had been touched, her hands fell accidentally on something else, a bundle she must have overlooked. Foolishly imagining it could be what she searched for, she pulled it out, only to find herself gasping in amazed consternation a few seconds later. The bulky envelopes contained what seemed to her most of her father's writings which she thought were sold.

With ice-cold hands she removed the contents of the top envelopes completely, the impersonal printed forms of publishers' rejection slips dancing before her dazed eyes. How did this all come to be here, in Luke Harrison's possession? And if her father's work hadn't sold who had paid for their supplies back on the island? She tried to tell herself she didn't know, but the answer was obvious.

'Tanya!' Luke's voice spun her ruthlessly as he came through the door. 'What are you doing there?'

'Nothing.' Swiftly she instinctively slumped sideways, hiding the manuscripts.

'Nothing? My God, you don't expect me to believe that!'

His eyes took in the dust on the floor, on her clothes as she knelt beside the open cupboard doors. 'There's dust on your face, everywhere.'

Why couldn't she think of something plausible? Her mind, still stunned by both her find and Luke's unexpected appearance, refused to give any explanation. She wished he would go away again instead of towering over her, his mouth compressed with his usual impatience. 'It will wash off.'

'Stop hedging, Tanya.' His eyes went to the heavy box in front of her. 'You weren't surely looking for a few trinkets to barter your way out of here?'

She was aware that the copra boat captains, some of them, would occasionally take goods instead of money for a lift to another island and she wished afterwards that she had had the wit to agree with Luke. Sense seemed to desert her and she could only look at him with angry, tormented eyes. 'You should have told me!'

'What should I have told you?' His anger faded warily.

'I've found my father's manuscripts, all of them returned.' Fumbling, she turned to pick up the untidy pile she had been sitting on. 'See!'

He saw all right and his mouth tightened grimly. 'So what? You've found the few that didn't quite make it. Nothing to get in a state about. Occasionally he sold something.'

Tanya stared at him, her blue eyes wide. 'Occasionally!' her young voice was hoarse with despair. 'I seem to recognise almost two years' work. It would have been kinder to have burnt it.'

'Probably,' there was a sudden hardness in the deep voice, 'but he asked me to keep them here. On my odd visits to you I took them with me and he went through them, but he sent them back with me rather than that you should know.'

'Why didn't you tell me, then?'

'Because you chose to keep out of my way. How could I talk with someone who was never around when I wanted her?'

She had the grace to flush, but this still didn't stop her repeating passionately, 'I still can't understand why you didn't destroy them.'

'I was foolish, perhaps,' he agreed. 'I imagined, strangely enough, that his daughter might one day ask for proof that they hadn't been sold.'

'And our supplies?' This was bothering her almost more than the manuscripts.

'I sent everything you needed with the copra boats and your father settled at the end of each year.'

'But these?' Almost tearfully she pointed to the pile at her feet. 'He can't have had any income from these. Didn't he realise?'

'Yes, but we considered it advisable that you didn't.'

'You mean we've been practically living off you for two years?'

His voice was perfectly hard and clear. 'And longer.'

Her cheeks seemed to burn with humiliation. He didn't believe in sparing her, nor did he feel an ounce of compassion, the way he looked at her under those dark satanic eyebrows. 'Charity,' she muttered bitterly. 'That's what it's called. That's what I've been living on!'

'Stop feeling so damned sorry for yourself. Helping a neighbour isn't looked on as charity in this part of the world. A lot of your father's stuff is good, but unfortunately, living as he did, it lacks verve. It—he reads too flat. If he hadn't chosen to live like a hermit he could have been an outstanding success. I must remind you, you didn't help. You were as content and seemingly unambitious as he was.'

'But I wouldn't have been had I known. I thought I was doing the right thing, and life was so pleasant.'

'Pleasant! You were wearing your fingers to the bone for a lost cause. Your father wanted a slave, not a daughter.' Luke's mouth was thinly drawn and momentarily he looked dangerous. 'You're fully conversant with most of the facts now. All I ask you to remember is that none of this was my doing. If you choose to go through my property while my back is turned then the fault is yours. You're entirely responsible if in the process you get hurt.'

'I'm sorry,' she choked, not able to confess the true reason why she had been going through his cupboards. This would have been too much like self-betrayal. Better he should think what he would. 'I was bored,' she offered feebly, knowing it a poor excuse.

'Really?'

She was sure he didn't believe her for an instant, his voice was too cynical. 'I just want to get back to England,' she pleaded miserably. 'If you'd help me?'

'Elizabeth would be upset.'

He hadn't exactly refused. 'It can't be long before her sister sends for her.'

'You can surely wait.'

His voice seemed slightly softer. Hope flared anew in her sore heart, in which the thought of leaving him flicked the pain. 'I would like to go at once. I don't want to stay getting deeper into your debt every day, on top of what you already seem to have done for my father and me.'

'Think about it,' Luke reached out a ruthless hand, drawing her to her feet, 'the amount of money you owe me. Some might well consider I've bought you, own you. I'm not unreasonable to insist that you stay here until you're out of my debt.'

'You're a beast!' Suddenly she could do nothing but scream at him, a release for searing emotions which threatened to tear her apart. 'You're despicable. I hate you!'

He grasped her thin shoulders and shook her, his face pale beneath his tan but adamant as he met her raging glance. 'At least you're feeling a positive emotion for a change. It's a healthier sign but not one which particularly frightens me, if that's what you are after. Let's just see how it develops, shall we?'

Her heart, as always when he touched her, beat too fast, forcing her to pause a moment to control her temper before she could speak again. 'You hope to get it all back with interest. I don't see how.'

'You don't because you haven't yet learnt to face facts. I have high hopes.'

'Because of Father's diaries?'

'Damn the diaries!' Luke was mildly explosive, then, to her surprise, cynically thoughtful. 'It could be an idea, though. Why don't you spend some of the energy you waste in trying to escape me in going through his material? You might be able to see it in a different light now. Spot where he went wrong. You have the use of a typewriter and free time in the afternoons while Elizabeth takes her siesta.'

'How do you know I don't take a siesta too?' she challenged unwisely.

'I happen to know exactly how you spend your afternoons.' He spoke with too much authority for Tanya to doubt it. 'You don't care to rest even when I suspect you could benefit from it. Maybe one day I'll be able to persuade you otherwise.'

Meeting the hard gleam at the back of his eyes, she flushed all over. He had mastered the art of conveying a lot behind a few careless words when it suited him! 'I'll have a look at them,' she agreed quickly, thinking the manuscripts a safer subject and lowering her eyes to them as they lay on the floor. But her nerves were taut and she had a curiously exhausted desire to cling to him, to confess she didn't want to leave him against his broad shoulder.

'I don't want you doing too much.' His hand curved her young cheek, then swept the heavy hair back off her smooth forehead as if he suddenly desired to read exactly what lay concealed under the rose-tinted skin. 'After Elizabeth has gone I have plans for you and I don't want you worn out.'

Unable to bear his nearness any longer, she jerked away from him and he let her go. She didn't ask him to explain his plans. He threatened her so often she didn't think it could be anything new. He simply believed in keeping her in revengeful suspense. His plans probably included an air ticket back to England just as soon as he

tired of provoking her, and while it wasn't comforting to
know she was regarded as a source of amusement if she had
patience he would undoubtedly release her in the end.

Luke departed again after collecting the papers he had
returned for in the first place and Tanya watched him go
with mixed feelings. The shock of coming inadvertently
across her father's work was taking its toll, and she felt
odd as she turned to stare at it again. She had looked for
Rowena's photograph and found something far worse. If
only she had known about this she might not have felt so
bitter. As it was she could scarcely bear to touch it. Possibly, when she had had time to pull herself together, she
might take Luke's advice and go through it, but she
doubted if she had either the talent or experience to re-
vise such work with any success.

Careless of the dust, she went down on her knees, sweeping the whole lot back into the spacious cupboards before
closing the doors. Then she rushed upstairs to hide her hot
tears against her pillow, giving way to the tearing anguish
within her that wouldn't seem to be relieved by any other
means.

Worn out with tears and unhappiness, she was almost
asleep when Toma came searching for her. Miss Logan
wished her to go to the lounge. Dismayed that she had been
in her room so long, Tanya hastily washed her tear-stained
face and did as she was bid. They had a visitor. She was
surprised to find a stranger talking to Miss Logan, a short,
rather stout man with a pleasant, tanned face. She concluded, as they turned when she entered the room, that he
had come from another island, that he had probably used
the air-strip a few miles from the house, where Luke kept
his plane.

Miss Logan, however, introduced him as a neighbour
who lived on the other end of this island. John Brown
shook Tanya's slim hand while she stared at him, unable
to keep the surprise from her eyes.

'I retired from Australia years ago,' he explained with

a twinkle. 'I knew Luke's father and he rented me a plot of land, and I've been here ever since.'

While Tanya bit her lip and wondered why no one had ever mentioned him, John Brown went on to say they had heard of her being here and that his wife was anxious to meet her.

This was yet another thing Luke had chosen not to tell her! He must have assumed she would try to enlist the Browns' help, maybe by pleading for a loan. It hurt that he had concluded that she had the nerve to ask this of strangers, yet her frown faded as she turned it over in her mind. Given a chance to get know the Browns she might be able to arrange something. It was a possibility, and that John Brown looked old enough to be her father, if not her grandfather, gave extra reassurance.

John Brown looked kindly and curious and he surveyed Tanya from under his bushy white eyebrows for a long time. He said Luke was dining with his wife and him the following evening and asked her to come along. He included Miss Logan in the invitation, but Elizabeth declined gracefully, murmuring lightly that she very rarely left the house these days.

Ten minutes later John went, after refusing a second drink, declaring he must get back as his wife was expecting visitors.

'I'm sure he only called to see what you're like,' Miss Logan said crossly after his truck drove away. 'I can't think what Luke's going to say!'

Tanya ignored this. 'You never mentioned anyone called Brown,' she exclaimed indignantly. 'I had no idea anyone lived on the island apart from Luke.'

'My dear, you do know about my memory!' Miss Logan was very reproachful. 'I forget such things.'

'But Luke does go out quite often. I thought he dined with his manager?'

'Sometimes he does,' Miss Logan nodded calmly, then added, to Tanya's utter surprise, 'There are others, you know. I expect you'll meet them all in good time.'

CHAPTER SIX

LUKE, when he heard of John Brown's visit, was not as
annoyed as Miss Logan had feared. Yet while he agreed
expressionlessly that Tanya might accompany him the
next evening he didn't satisfy her growing curiosity regarding the other families on the island until they were actually
on their way.

'There are only two more,' he told her, 'so it's nothing to
get excited about. One is a lone writer, like your father,
but he isn't here very often. He's away just now, but when
he is here he lives in a small cabin about a mile from the
Browns.'

'And the other?'

'Another retired couple.'

'You never told me!' Her glance skimmed his shoulders,
coming to rest widely upon his chiselled profile that immediately hardened.

'If I set it all down there'd still be something you'd
accuse me of missing out. Why should I have told you? I
might have done eventually, but I didn't want you breaking
your neck. It's over ten miles to the Browns' place and
they're nearest. Ten miles over suicidal roads, which in
one of your reckless moods you might have attempted.'

'Did your wife visit these neighbours?' Why did she have
to ask him such senseless questions concerning Rowena!

'Naturally,' his sigh was that of an adult dealing with
a particularly tiresome child. 'She and Edna are friends.'

'I see.' She noticed, with an odd sinking feeling, he
spoke as if Rowena was still around.

'No, you don't, Tanya. You're too young to understand
a lot of things. The feelings of a man who had a marriage
which wasn't a marriage. You might be more than apprehensive if you did.'

She hated him for being so cruel and mocking, hated and loved him. She glanced at him again, as he pressed savagely on, her eyes dark with secret longing. She must be mistaken about many things, especially of loving him. Her imagination must be playing her tricks. It couldn't happen like this after just a few short weeks! Tonight he was dressed impeccably in a dark suit with a white shirt and looked darkly handsome. He had told her earlier to wear something pretty, and curiously eager to please him for once she had searched through the large wardrobe of clothes in her room until her hands had rested unerringly on a long swathe of softly coloured chiffon. It was a lovely dress with a matching stole, the wide skirt fluttering about her slender limbs, the tiered top clinging seductively to her shapely breast in folds of gauzy transparency. Her hair she had brushed until it shone and left lying simply across her shoulders. She wore no make-up except for a little pale lip gloss on her mobile mouth and a hint of blue shadow to deepen her eyes almost to purple.

The one thing she missed was some perfume, perhaps a spray of cologne, a simple refreshing fragrance. Without it she felt youthful, unsophisticated, unsure even of her appearance. Luke hadn't said anything when she had walked rather nervously down the stairs towards him, but he hadn't seemed to miss a single detail of her appearance.

She sat in silence as they approached the bungalow, her hands clenched tightly, one on the other, as if to still an inward trembling. The dwelling was set against a background of rocky crags and there was a pearly mist over the lagoon facing it. The slight mist brought a heavenly coolness to the purple shadows beneath the palm trees, as the trade winds dropped and dusk fell softly over the land. In a village they just passed, fishermen were home with the day's catch and there had been the smell of the evening meal cooking. The noise of happy laughter had mingled with the crackle of fires and children playing. Several had stopped what they were doing, stepping forward to see the big white boss and his young guest pass, and while they waved the air had seemed to pulse with the scent of flowers.

Luke shot a glance from Tanya's pale face to the watch strapped on his lean wrist. 'Just in time,' his eyes came back to her keenly. 'I don't know what sort of figure you intend to cut, but let me warn you it won't do to try and enlist the Browns' sympathy. I've already explained about you.'

'What have you been telling them?' She turned to him, her eyes full of hostility.

'Never mind.' Whatever he had said it didn't seem to affect his conscience. 'They realise your being here is for your own good, so don't attempt to concoct situations that don't exist.'

They swept into the compound before she could collect her scattered thoughts. Without knowing what he had told the Browns her hands were tied. He was diabolical, a scheming devil! She had indeed been composing various contriving little speeches in her head and he had guessed, clipping her wings, with a few calculated words, as if they had as much substance as a butterfly's. It made everything she had so carefully rehearsed impossible to put into practice, especially with strangers.

Luke saw, too, that she never got a chance to be alone with either of their hosts. They were only just in time for dinner, something he had apparently judged to the last minute. When they arrived he kept hold of her arm after removing the light stole from her shoulders himself, giving the impression that she had no need to journey to a bedroom to take it off. The meal itself was a long-drawn-out affair with Luke, charmingly affable, leading the Browns on to talk of themselves rather than the silent girl who faced him. Long after certain subjects might have dwindled he kept them going, and she suspected he did so deliberately. Occasionally she could cheerfully have trodden on the foot that lay so near her own under the narrow table.

Afterwards they had coffee brought by the usual retinue of silent-footed servants. While it might be very pleasant to be waited on thus, Tanya would have given anything just then for an ordinary English household, where she might have offered to help Mrs Brown with the washing up. In the sanctuary of a cosy kitchen she might have poured out at least some of her troubles.

As it was, when Edna Brown asked how long she was staying, Tanya felt too nervous, with Luke clamped to her side on a small sofa, to murmur anything but that she wasn't sure. When Edna went on to enquire sympathetically about her father and if she had enjoyed living on such a small place as Karowi, Luke answered. He also answered the following few questions Edna directed at her.

'Can't you let Tanya reply for herself?' Edna, a stout matron with more than her share of self-importance, frowned at Luke reproachfully. 'It's not as if she hadn't a tongue in her head.'

'Luke ordered me to pretend I haven't,' with a faint smile Tanya joined in the attack. 'It saves him the bother of correcting me, if I don't say anything.'

'The trouble with Luke,' Edna added audaciously, 'is that he's getting rather uncivilised. I can't think what will happen when Elizabeth goes. He ought to marry again.'

If her indirect remarks were aimed at Luke he was more than competent to deal with them. His mouth quirked. 'I could be wiser to continue on my own,' he drawled, 'unless someone like Tanya here would take me on.'

Was this his way of avenging himself because she had been too outspoken? Tanya's softly rounded chin came up, her eyes sparkling with an unusual daring, perhaps due to the fact that she had been reckless enough to drink two glasses of John's innocent-tasting wine. Luke's sardonic observations hurt irrationally, though she didn't know why. Forcing herself to meet his glinting eyes, she retorted, 'It must take a lot of co-operation to make a good marriage. I wonder why it so often is that the woman tires first?'

She saw his face darken as he guessed accurately that she was hinting at his own marriage with Rowena. 'Perhaps because she is a woman,' he jeered softly, his taunting smile for Tanya alone.

Edna, as if she too would have liked to shake Luke's hard equilibrium, interposed sweetly, 'Have you heard from dear Rowena lately, Luke?'

'Not for a while,' he replied, looking at her levelly.

John Brown intervened, as if he considered his wife's pointed queries less than tactful. 'Elizabeth seems a great deal better. Is she still leaving?'

'She's improved a lot since Tanya came,' Luke nodded, 'but she'll still be better with her sister.'

Edna smiled with bright curiosity. 'Does this mean Tanya will be going as well?'

'Not necessarily.'

No one, it appeared, dared ask why there should be any doubt; even Edna's determination seemed momentarily to fail her. When Luke Harrison's green eyes were cool it took courage to continue to goad him. Tanya, by this time familiar with his enigmatical remarks, schooled herself to take no notice, yet felt her cheeks flush as Edna's face lit with cautious speculation.

'It can't be much fun for Tanya, Luke, isolated as you are in that great house with no people of her own age for company.'

Tanya started, then was surprised to hear herself protesting, when she might have made the most of an opportunity to annoy Luke yet again, 'I don't mind, really, Mrs Brown. I'm very fortunate to be there.'

'I understand, my dear.' Edna's gaze softened but flickered suspiciously again as Luke's arm, which had lain along the back of the sofa, dropped lightly to Tanya's shoulder. Edna seemed to take a deep breath. 'You must still be feeling sad, dear, because of your father, but all sorrow eases eventually. Think of your own, Luke, when Rowena left! Soon, Tanya, you'll find this island too quiet.'

'I've weighed up all the disadvantages.' Luke's hand tightened hurtfully on Tanya's slight shoulder, causing her to shiver involuntarily as he pulled her closer. His fingers curved the fragile bone insistently for all to see, and his voice conveyed a subtle satisfaction. Tanya suspected he deliberately intended to shock Edna.

Maybe this was why Tanya made no great effort to evade Luke's encircling arm, which must have given the impression of a greater intimacy than ever existed. She knew a faint resentment herself at the way Edna jumped to the wrong conclusions.

A moment later, as if having no inclination to give any of them the chance of saying more, Luke said they must go. He released Tanya, with seeming reluctance, and rose to his feet.

'Poor child.' Edna's smile was still fixed brightly as she saw them off. 'If you ever need help or advice come to me.'

On their way home, when Luke asked savagely if Tanya had enjoyed the outing she had so coveted, she said she had. She didn't add that she was trying desperately not to think of Edna's remarks about Rowena, the knowledge they had brought, whether intentionally or not, that Luke still had some communication with his ex-wife. Perhaps he still took her out, when he was away from the island? Many men enjoyed a good friendship with their divorced wives. Maybe Rowena liked Luke better now she wasn't actually married to him. There would be excitement, danger without ties. Strangely enough the latter was what Tanya found herself suddenly longing for. To know the security of really belonging to someone. Of waking up in the morning close to someone like Luke, of sleeping held tightly in his arms. When Luke Harrison was near there was inside her a yearning, one she didn't completely understand.

'What did you think of Edna?' Luke interrupted her thoughts.

'I'm not sure,' Tanya managed to sound cool and collected and she hoped it disguised a more anguished uncertainty as they drove on through the night.

'Edna's all right providing you don't take her too seriously,' he replied sardonically. 'You don't have to worry about the Browns. They're returning to Australia next year.

I think being so far from all their relatives is beginning to
bother them at last.'

'Everyone seems to be going but me,' Tanya retorted,
unable to keep the bitterness from her voice. Luke didn't
love her, but he wouldn't let her leave. 'Even Rowena
escaped you!'

'Shut up!' he rejoined harshly, the angle of his hard
jaw tightening in the darkness so clearly that in fear Tanya
subsided into silence, looking away.

She didn't see much of Luke for the next few days, but
this could have been because she did her best to avoid him.
This wasn't difficult as he was busy and Miss Logan kept
her occupied fetching and carrying, small jobs the servants
might have done but which Tanya performed without
complaint. It gave her an excuse not to pursue her father's
manuscripts, for she was too restless to settle properly to
anything. All her free time was spent on the beach and in
the sea. There she swam until she was exhausted. Then she
would lie beneath the palm trees until sufficiently recovered
to wash the grains of sand from off her smooth body before
wandering back to the house.

Once, when Miss Logan was resting, she went down to
the village. Not until then did she learn inadvertently
through Jules that the Browns had been away from the
island and brought a visitor back with them. Jules had
hesitated there, suddenly changing the subject with undue
haste, so it was not until before dinner one evening that
Tanya discovered the visitor was Rowena.

Toma told her as she lingered while Tanya dressed. The
girl had begged to be allowed to do Tanya's long hair and
Tanya, feeling she couldn't keep on refusing, said she
might. Toma brushed it, then arranged it deftly on top of
Tanya's small head so that it gave her height, then softened
the rather severe effect with a few enchanting ringlets.
These just touched the pale curve of Tanya's cheek.

As she worked Toma's skilful fingers were surprisingly
soothing, but Tanya found nothing soothing in what she

said! 'Missus Rowena has come back. Maybe the boss and she marry again.'

Tanya sat very still feeling herself slowly turning to stone. Somehow she had never expected that Rowena would return. As for marrying Luke again—well, why not, if he still loved her? 'You would like that?' she asked Toma.

'We want only that Mister Luke is happy,' Toma chanted in her broken English. 'Miss Elizabeth not like it, maybe? When boss marry Miss Rowena before, she go away.'

'I see.' Tanya frowned anxiously. Elizabeth had never mentioned this. She might have criticised idly, but she had never actually spoken ill of Rowena.

'Miss Elizabeth plenty sad, and mad.'

'Toma, you must have been too young to remember!'

Toma's eyes were huge black orbs of indignation, 'I was too young, Miss Tanya, but my mother, everyone, they remember. We also know everything. We know when people are happy or sad. We know when they are in love, when they sleep together.'

Had it been true, then, that during the latter years of their marriage Luke and his wife hadn't shared the same bedroom? Miss Logan had delicately hinted at this, but Tanya found it difficult to believe that a man as virile as Luke Harrison would tolerate such a condition. Unless he hadn't minded, of course. It could have been Rowena's stipulation if he hadn't been faithful to her.

'The knowing of these things is in our bones and blood,' Toma vowed cheerfully, mistaking Tanya's silence for doubt.

'I'm quite aware of your black magic,' Tanya said severely. 'I'm not a total stranger, Toma.'

'In some ways you are different,' Toma conceded, 'but not wiser. We island people have learnt to accept. You fight the fate our Gods chose for you. You wish to leave us, yet our most wise doctor say you stay and have many children.'

Mercifully Toma was called by Miss Logan before Tanya was forced to hear more, but her cheeks were still warm as

she ran downstairs. She forgot, in her confusion, to remain
in her room until the last minute in order not to see Luke
alone.

He was on his own and she could have flown again to
find him standing in the lounge, a drink in his hand, looking, if it had been anyone else but him, as though he was in
need of it.

'Well?' his mocking gaze flicked her disturbed face.
'Something has obviously scared you more than the
thoughts of a few minutes alone with me.'

Unconsciously drawing nearer to him, she shivered. Outside it was dark and only one light was switched on in the
large room. It glowed softly but cast shadows which
strangely unnerved her. A flying beetle smashed against the
shade and visibly she started, curiously on edge. She knew
he wouldn't believe if she denied she was a little nervous.

'I've been listening to Toma, I'm afraid. I should know
better. It's not exactly what she said ...' Tanya hesitated,
finding suddenly she could repeat none of it.

'So you've felt the beat of our South Seas mysticism,' he
quipped dryly, placing a glass firmly in her trembling
hands.

'You don't have to make it sound like a smart musical
comedy!'

'I don't want to frighten you more. We could be wiser
to keep it light.' His dark brows rose sceptically. 'Just what
has she been saying to put you in a state of mild panic?'

How could she tell him about Rowena? Or to speak of
her arrival unless he mentioned it himself. He must know
Rowena was here. He had an inexplicably brooding air
about him tonight. When she had come through the door-
way he had seemed lost in some kind of contemplation—as
if his mind lingered on something—or someone, just beyond
his reach.

Tanya's own mind whirled wildly as she sought some
explanation far removed from her. 'It was nothing, really.
It must have been the way she said it. She swears the
doctor in the village knows most things before he's told.'

'Or thinks he does.'

'You don't believe, then?' Relief moved through her.

'I've no reason not to.' Her relief was shortlived as Luke said evenly, 'The good doctor is retired. He has good medical qualifications, but he has always had extreme faith in his clairvoyant instincts and has often been proved right. While I wouldn't lose any sleep about it, I shouldn't advise you to dismiss it all as sheer claptrap.'

'Does he tell you everything?'

'No, Tanya, so you don't have to look as if you're drowning. Your secrets are safe. He considers a young girl's head full of only one thing—romance, men.'

Tanya managed to look supremely indifferent even while a faint colour ran under her clear skin.

Luke's glint of amusement faded. 'The doctor and I have a sort of working relationship which doesn't include a daily forecast of what's to happen or what's going on. These people live by their senses, but for someone who is not exactly one of them it can be a dangerous game.'

Luke spoke so smoothly and the light was so dim it would be impossible to judge what he was really thinking. Surely, in spite of what he said, he must know Rowena was here? Staring into his enigmatical green eyes, Tanya suddenly knew he did, just as she realised he had no intention of discussing Rowena with anyone.

Instead, he held her widening gaze for fully half a minute before changing the subject abruptly. 'Why have you been avoiding me?'

'I haven't.' She was eager to talk of something different, but not this.

He treated her reply with the contempt it deserved. 'Is it because I didn't tell you you looked beautiful, the other evening, in your enticing dress? Or because I didn't round the night off by making love to you? By picking you up when you stumbled as you left the truck and carrying you straight up to bed.'

'You know,' she gasped painfully, 'that's the last place I'd want to go to!'

'I was talking of your bed, not mine,' he taunted out-rageously. 'Women always have a one-track mind.'

She flinched as if he had struck her, her cheeks paling. It was the devil in him which could hold her terrified as she had no idea how to deal with it. He could be savage, even ruthless, and then she trembled. He tried to believe some women were dependable and innocent, but he didn't always succeed. More often than not he chose to think the worst of them, and to lash with his tongue was the next best thing to laying his hands on them. Only to those whom he had known all his life, who like Miss Logan had proved their absolute reliability, did he perhaps give his trust. In the meanwhile, like the tiger ready to pounce when it suited him on his shivering victim, he would continue to be cruel. It made it imperative to hide the fact that she had wanted him to say she looked nice and that, later, the startling revelation that she had suddenly yearned to be in his arms had made her stumble. She had wanted to feel his lips on hers again, his hands on her body ...

'I don't expect you to pay me compliments,' she cried, drawing a trembling breath, 'nor to carry me upstairs. I expect you're reserving such an honour for Rowena!'

She was unprepared for the way his face came alive with near anger and shrank back from him apprehensively. 'Sorry,' she gulped, the briefness of that making it sound as though she wasn't sorry at all. What on earth had made her mention Rowena? It must have been that she had been so busy thinking of her. A protraction of thought.

Luke caught hold of her shoulders as she swayed back in alarm. 'So this is what you've been trying to hide! I guessed there was something more than what you've al-ready confessed to. Toma told you she's here?'

'Well, she ...'

'Stop worrying,' his temper cooled as quickly as it had arisen, but his voice was still harsh. 'I'd have told you myself if I'd thought you'd be interested—if you'd asked.'

Her shoulders shook slightly beneath his clasp and she drew a funny little breath, enquiring with a childlike audacity but which contained too much pain to be anything but adult, 'Why has she come, now that you're divorced?'

He shrugged indifferently, his eyes oddly watchful on Tanya's whitening face. 'I can't stop her, she's a free agent. Maybe she has a sudden hunger to survey what she discarded. Women are nothing if not tenacious, my dear.'

'It's your island . . .'

'You could say.' His hands left her shoulders, as if the thought of another's interested him more. 'The Browns, however, pay a legitimate rent which gives them the right to have what guests they choose.'

Far from convinced, Tanya felt her throat close, forgetting it was none of her business. He talked of being discarded, but she had a notion it had been the other way around. She was also sure he could make it relatively impossible for anyone to come here if he didn't want them to. Which must mean he had no objection to Rowena. More likely it indicated that he had a real desire to see her again and pain rose like a live thing in Tanya's cold breast.

'Will she be coming here?' Again the question might have been better not asked, but she couldn't withhold it.

'For a girl who only wants to leave me you're over anxious about a lot of things concerning my private affairs,' he taunted. 'The possibility is there. I might even ask her to call when I see her. She might have changed. To contemplate such an eventuality might add a little spice to life.'

Bitterly Tanya regarded him. Didn't he know anyone could pretend to change for the better? He sounded as if he was prepared to welcome Rowena warmly, to make excuses one way and another for the breakdown of their marriage. Tanya wanted to shout that he deserved all he got, but a murmur of voices on the stairs warned her of Miss Logan's approach.

'I hope you're going to be pleasantly surprised,' she hissed, despair turning her regrettably feline.

'Small cat!' he laughed easily into her wide, tilted eyes. 'Come here, before you scratch.' Before she could stop him he caught her swiftly to him, his hard mouth parting hers with such force she tasted blood on her teeth. Her head snapped back with a low moan, her hands clutched air wildly, but before she could touch him she was free. 'It's the only way to treat a cat,' he jeered. 'Surprise it, before it can unsheath its claws.'

Miss Logan must have heard about Rowena's visit as she kept glancing at Luke all through dinner. Afterwards he went out, and Tayna's heart sank as she concluded that he must be on his way to visit Rowena. If the Browns hadn't asked him for dinner they would undoubtedly welcome him for coffee and drinks. Perhaps later he and Rowena might wander along the shore with only the soft music of the wind and waves to accompany them and, as he said, the rediscovery of each other would be exciting. He wouldn't kiss Rowena as he did her, as if he wanted to break her almost in two. For someone who must evoke so many memories his caress would be tender. Rowena would have no reason to nearly faint from the pain of arms and a mouth that hurt savagely!

After Luke had gone Miss Logan grew mildly agitated. She was inclined to at this hour and, aware of it herself, usually went straight to bed. There, with the aid of a mild sedative and warm drink, she slept quietly until the next morning. This evening, as soon as the door closed behind Luke, instead of preparing to go upstairs she began worrying about Rowena. As Tanya suspected, Elizabeth had learnt from Toma that she was on the island.

'I wonder how long it will be, child, before she turns up here?'

Tanya, who felt she had had about enough of Rowena for one day, persuaded Miss Logan that she would be wiser to go to bed than to stay downstairs worrying about something that might not happen. 'She might not come,' she said, more hopelessly than she knew.

'She could upset me.' Elizabeth, her face puckering anxiously, gathered up her knitting.

'I won't let her,' Tanya promised, wondering helplessly

how she could stop Rowena doing anything she chose.

'No good will come of it,' Miss Logan sighed, as Tanya handed her over to the waiting Toma. 'She'll only make Luke unhappy.'

Long after Miss Logan had said goodnight, Tanya wandered about her own room. Restless and unsure of herself, she would liked to have gone down to the beach. There she might have swum until she forgot all about Luke and Rowena. It was only because Miss Logan might have one of her nightmares and want her that she didn't do it. Instead she made do with a shower, which didn't seem to induce the longed-for oblivion at all. A kind of unbearable pain was battering her head, the hurt of it creeping right through her until she could do nothing but lie and shiver.

At last, a half sob mingling strangely with an impatient sigh, she got out of her tumbled bed and cautiously opened her door. After making sure there was no one in the wide passage outside she slipped silently along to Luke's room. She didn't think about what she was doing; if she had she knew she would never have made it. The house was quiet; he had not come home yet; when he did she would hear the noise of his engine which she had listened to many times before. If he was with Rowena he might be late. They would have plenty to talk about.

Now that Rowena was here Tanya could resist the desire to see what she looked like no longer. It had hit her like a sudden inspiration that if Luke still loved Rowena he must keep her photograph near him, the most likely place being his bedroom, away from over-curious eyes. It was dark inside his room as she crept through the door, the faint light from the moon coming through the window not sufficient to enable her to see clearly. With trepid fingers she switched on a light—and there it was.

A photograph of a woman on top of the tallboy against the far wall, where the gleam of the frame matched that of the fine old mahogany. A position not too conspicuous, which under the circumstances was understandable. That it was there at all must be cause for some speculation, apart from her own. Standing on tiptoe, Tanya reached up and brought it down, noting, as it came within her line of vision, Rowena's signature sprawled along the bottom. With some misgivings she carried it to where she could see it properly.

Rowena was undoubtedly beautiful, a pale-headed woman with strong features, yet there was something about her that Tanya could barely define. A quality in the glossy face that stared back at her which faintly repulsed. About the eyes and mouth was a unmistakable hardness, or so it seemed to Tanya. The mouth was thin, the twisted smile looking as if it might be habitual, holding a hint of cruelty. Searching it, she could find little warmth anywhere.

Tanya's spirits plunged sharply. Every time Luke glanced at Rowena he must see this for himself, and if such visible defects counted so little with him must it not prove he still loved Rowena very much? And wasn't it significant that she was back? If Luke was fond of her still, and starved of affection, might he not, as Toma had suggested, ask her to marry hin. again? He wouldn't be the first man to marry the same woman twice.

Her limbs almost gave way beneath her as she slumped down on Luke's bed, something she would have been aghast to find herself doing if she had wholly realised. The photograph still clutched in her hands, she continued to stare down at it. What would Miss Logan do if this happened? Her sister was still unable to take her, it could be weeks yet before Miss Logan could go to her, but if Rowena lived here again Miss Logan wouldn't be allowed to stay. Neither, with friendship non-existent between the two women, would Miss Logan be able to return occasionally for the holidays Luke had promised her. Just knowing Luke was married again to Rowena would worry the heart out of Miss Logan wherever she might be.

Pushing a hand wearily over her eyes, Tanya gazed blindly at Luke's former wife, the woman who threatened to entice him again. She felt it her duty, if only because she must owe him a lot, to wait up for him, to convince him that he must not make the same mistake twice—that

Rowena would never make him happy. Small sentences came awkwardly to her tired mind, to be rejected and composed again. The minutes ticked by as she assured herself it was solely on Miss Logan's behalf that she waited here feeling crucified. Her heavy lids began to droop, a tear glittering on her long lashes, and seeking comfort, she turned her head into Luke's pillow where the sharp scent of his after-shave cologne still lingered. Deeply she breathed it, filling her starved senses with the masculine tang of it, and when sleep descended suddenly she didn't fight it but only clung to the pillow closer, with an unconscious, intangible longing.

How long she slept there she had no idea. When first she became aware of someone shaking her gently she felt nothing but a niggling resentment.

'Go away,' she muttered, scarcely stirring.

'I would, if you didn't happen to be in my bed.'

My bed? Luke! Oh no! Terrified, she came awake faster than she could ever remember doing before. It was still dark, the light she had left burning had been switched off and through the window there came only the first gleamings of the early dawn. She could see him by the bed, bending over her, tall and broad in what looked like a silk dressing gown.

'Please!' She sat up, staring at him, not knowing what she was pleading for so urgently as her dazed eyes encountered his enigmatical ones in the dimness of the room. With a kind of numb instinctiveness she pulled the sheets higher around her trembling body as she realised with a terrible embarrassment exactly where she was.

She whispered, a nerve pulsing visbly in her throat, 'I'm sorry, I can explain.' She couldn't—not truthfully, and suspected he knew it, but she had to say something.

He settled his weight on the bed beside her without removing his eyes from her frightened face. If he sensed her tormented nerves he had no pity for them. 'I could be due an explanation,' he said mildly, 'if only because you appear to have appropriated my bed. I can't say I appreciate coming home in the early hours and finding my room taken over without any previous indication. If you hadn't been such a naïve little innocent I might have thought it an invitation. As it was I decided your bed must do in exchange, but unfortunately it was in too much of a heap to offer much comfort. Instead I made do with the one next door, but I haven't slept. Thinking of you here didn't exactly help. Do you deliberately set out to torment me, girl?'

His voice was harsh again and Tanya flinched back on the pillows, finding them softer by far than his expression. Momentarily she forgot the explanation, the reason she sought and couldn't find for her presence here. 'You didn't have to come and wake me just because you were restless yourself, and if you were you shouldn't blame me!'

'Well, that's certainly a mouthful,' he jeered, 'just because I had the decency to come and wake you before anyone discovers you?'

She refused to be appeased. 'You mean you wouldn't want Rowena to know?' Tanya couldn't bear to call her Mrs Harrison, the name she was legally entitled to use as she had never reverted to her maiden name or married again.

Luke's lip curled. 'Haven't you done enough damage already? You enter my room, smash her photograph, the only one I have, then calmly go to sleep on my bed.'

'I didn't smash anything!' Tanya was shocked.

'Yes. I picked up the pieces. You probably dropped it as you fell asleep, but don't look so surprised.'

'I'm sorry, I was just seeing what she was like.' She turned her head sideways, knowing she should be feeling ashamed. 'You'll be able to take another now, won't you?'

'Certainly.'

Did he have to speak so authoritatively, as if he had his future well and truly mapped out and didn't care, one way or another, for the shivering girl by his side. Her thoughts swerving drunkenly, she realised incredulously she was under the sheet, not on top of it as she had been when she

. had fallen asleep, and that Luke must have put her there. The blood thundered through her veins. 'You should have dumped me on my own bed.'

'I did try, but you hung on to this one and I didn't feel equal to the struggle.'

'You were late. You were seeing Rowena?'

'I saw her.'

'Luke?' Her eyes enormous with inner tension, Tanya asked, 'Are you going to marry her again?'

'A man gets lonely.'

She could tell nothing from his tone, but it must mean he was considering it. Panic and an aching sense of loss speared wildly through her. She sat up straighter, leant nearer to him, her eyes fixed compulsively to the large, dark shape of him. 'Is it a wife, or are you just lonely for—for a woman?'

Through the dim light, as she sat trembling at her own audaciousness, she imagined she saw his mouth twitch. 'The latter would do,' he drawled, 'but Rowena would never do anything without a wedding ring.'

Desperately Tanya fought the voice which warned her to stop right there, but there was also something stronger inside her driving her on. It was crazy, as if she were coming face to face with herself and she was staring at a stranger. 'Luke,' she laid a nervously daring hand on his arm, 'I know Miss Logan doesn't care for Rowena, but she does like me—at least I think she does. What's just as important, I like her.'

'So?' he prompted, his eyes glittering, not giving her any help.

'So ...' She felt like someone dying, having to moisten her dry lips before she could get it out. Even then it came in odd little jerks and she was grateful for the darkness which hid her worsening agitation. 'Luke,' she began again, 'if it's only a woman you want, why not have me? Surely I would do—unless you love Rowena to distraction?'

CHAPTER SEVEN

TANYA might have dropped a bomb that killed all sound. After the first shattering impact there was total silence. A cold, disapproving silence, she thought, with Luke muttering suddenly beneath his breath. What, she couldn't quite make out, but it had a harsh ring to it and he made no attempt to touch her.

His brief laughter didn't sound too good either. 'What fine spirit of self-sacrifice brought this on?' he quipped curtly. 'You offer yourself for Elizabeth's sake—the girl who couldn't wait to get away from me!'

Tanya's voice trembled, betraying her. 'I owe you a lot. I owe Elizabeth too in a way, and I've nothing really to go back to England for. I know I've pretended I have ...'

His hands went out and it hurt as he gripped her bare shoulders over the narrow straps of her thin nightgown. 'So let's take this one step at a time. 'You imagine I'm going to reinstate Rowena and this will upset Elizabeth? In order to avoid this you agree to live with me. Is this as far as you've got? Have you given a thought to what could happen?'

'You mean ...' Feeling worse by the minute, Tanya couldn't look at him, not even through the darkness. Her whole body grew hot with confusion.

He didn't believe in sparing her, although her tautness must have got through to him, 'Yes, I do mean you could get pregnant. It would be very likely. Maybe I wouldn't allow you Rowena's tricks!'

Tanya wished she could sink right out of sight, or that she could borrow some of his detached impassiveness. He might have been lecturing a promiscuous teenager, while she had only been trying to save him from his own folly. She tried to find words to tell him this, but none could get through the tightness of her throat.

Transfixed, she stared at him, in her eyes a kind of torment he couldn't or wouldn't see. He seemed intent only to go on punishing her. 'What will you do when I send you packing? I might keep the child, but not you.'

'No ...' A kind of slow anguish beginning to take over, she buried her shaking face in her hands. How could any man be so cruel! How could any girl be so depraved—for this was what she must have been to have made such an offer! Yet she would never have made it if she hadn't loved him, and been concerned for Elizabeth. It hadn't sprung from a shallow need for excitement. She felt burnt up now with horror and humiliation, but for all this the idea persisted. Wouldn't a few months of happiness be better than years with nothing to remember? And if it did happen, as he said, might she not manage to escape before he could take anything from her?

Luke's own face was a mask, then, as if taking her silence for pleading, he pulled her closer. 'Tanya?'

Startled, her eyes flew open as panic swept her. How had she thought this sort of thing could be easy? He was older and experienced, yet as soon as she was in his arms she was lost under a wave of desire which was more of a devastation than pleasure. It was early morning, the night hadn't been long, but her body felt rested, all too ready to respond to her wayward senses. Sensation was moving through her softly and her eyes, densely blue through heavy lashes, clung to his as if needing to read his every expression.

'Tanya,' he touched her cheek with a lean finger, 'I'm going to be your lover, have no doubts about that.' On his face was a cynical sparkle. 'You don't care for me, but you have no other means of paying your debts. You admit there's nothing for you in England and you're very comfortable here. Only now that Rowena has come both you and Elizabeth are frightened you'll be thrown out. That's it, isn't it?'

'Something like that.' He was so near she found it difficult to speak, especially as his hand was gently tugging aside the protective sheet she still clutched to her chin. Didn't he intend giving her time? She had thought they could lead up to a closer relationship slowly over the next weeks, but sensing in him a deliberate insistence she felt the first tremors of doubt. 'Luke,' the tortured breath she released hit his cheek and bounced back, 'perhaps we could discuss everything better in the morning?'

'It is morning.' His voice was deceptively quiet as he bent his mouth to her bared shoulder and she shuddered as the blood whipped through her veins. His dark face closed up. 'You didn't think I would agree to wait?'

She could feel the smoothness of his taut muscles moving against her and moved, with instinctive innocence, away from him. 'You don't understand . . .'

She opened her lips to protest at the precise moment he lifted and lowered his head, and as his mouth enclosed hers all her former reluctance shattered like glass into sparkling shreds which fell as stardust against her tightly closed lips. There was violence in the way he pressed her down into the softness of the mattress and all the yearnings of the last lonely years in her response. For a brief second his mouth left hers, moving over the soft skin of her cheeks and throat before returning to hers again, his first assault giving way to a slower, deeper hunger.

He thrust his fingers through her brown silken hair until the angle of her head was exactly where he wanted it, his other hand pulling aside her nightdress, nothing gentle about it now as it sought the full curves below, crushing her to him.

Her body began to quiver with the deep tremors that hit it, and unable to resist she curled her slender young arms tightly around his strong neck, her heart pounding. When she stirred he thought she was still protesting.

'Tanya,' he groaned, 'be still. Do you realise what you're doing to me? I want you, and that you want me too seems a miracle. For too long your slender body has been a torment.'

Words, whispered thickly and passionately against her

parted lips as she lay back on the pillows, her thick burnished hair spread over them, her breath fervent, unsteady with the released force of untried emotions.

It was the very force of these which terrified her and she must have cried out, for he lifted his head. 'Luke!' One of her arms slid from his neck and she flung it blindly over her eyes. Where was her panic coming from? How could passion be mixed so subtly with doubt, fear and pain? It was as if her mind fought with her body and they were two entirely separate entities, quite divorced from one another. She wanted to love Luke completely, but not like this. It went against everything she had been brought up to believe—she wouldn't use the word principles, it had too antiquated a ring about it. When she was a child her mother had been very strict, instilling certain rules of conduct. If Tanya hadn't spent two years out here she wasn't sure if she could have lived by them. She was perhaps more what circumstances had made her. Even so, she hadn't realised her inhibitions went so deep. Or was it because she loved Luke Harrison that the hope of a more permanent relationship other than the one she had unrealistically suggested would not allow her to besmirch the only gift she had to bring it?

Luke must give her time to come to terms with herself, if not him. She forgot how all this had come about in the first place. 'Luke?' She didn't know if he was listening, or if he was that he would be prepared to take any notice. She wasn't even sure she wanted him to. 'Please, Luke?'

At last it got through; the slight stiffening of her too responsive body, the sudden twist that took her a few inches away from him. 'All I want is a little time.'

'For what?' It was frightening, the immediate hardness of his query.

'Just to get used to the idea, and you, maybe.'

'Used to it!' the pearly light from the sea was stronger, clearly pinpointing every pleading curve of her face. His laughter held no mirth. 'You mean time to think of a good excuse?'

'No—I . . .'

'You might well say you haven't the guts to finish what you began!'

She shivered. She had never seen him so suddenly angry, a cold fury that put glittery lights behind his brilliant gaze. 'It's not quite like that, Luke . . .'

'No?' He caught her savagely, flinging her back from him across the pillow, so she thought she might break. 'Don't you think it's time you stopped playing around, time you grew up? Out here, where there's blood in a man's veins, it could be essential. You have nice cosy ideas that make you feel good but a man like hell—when you have no intention of going through with them!'

She was wretched now, frozen by a dull, resigned kind of misery. 'You should have let me go, before I got involved with Elizabeth—and Rowena and—and you.'

'You don't have to whisper, as if there was something the matter with your throat.' He rolled off the bed, his feet hitting the floor with deadly emphasis. 'What should I have done? Thrown you to the wolves? You probably wouldn't have made the first stage of your journey. Now get out of my sight before I release the last curbs on my restraint!' A swift movement, a twist of his powerful limbs, and he leant down again, hands clamped on either side of her cowardly, shivering body. 'Then, I might tell you, nothing would save you. Now, out!'

In the end he allowed her to hang on to her remaining shred of dignity by swiftly picking up his dressing gown and walking out himself, muttering curtly that he was taking a shower, should she wish to join him again.

His sarcasm made her anguish complete as she stumbled to follow, if not in the same direction. In her own room she flung herself into her armchair, the tears she had held rigidly back coursing down her white cheeks. Hadn't she made a mess of everything! Never would she be able to face Luke again—or herself, for that matter. Was it ever pleasant to be forced to see oneself as one really was? She had thought herself an ice-maiden. The odd times Luke had kissed her she had been a bit carried away, but not enough to arouse a proper apprehension. In his bed there had been a thunderous passion, studded with flashing slivers of lightning she had never known existed. Held close to him as she had been, she had felt entirely wanton, so much so she had been as terrified of her own reactions as his.

She could laugh now to think of her own foolishness, how the cool little deal she had thought up on the spur of the moment had disintegrated before her very eyes. Painfully she scrubbed at her still streaming face. It had all moved so swiftly beyond her control, and somehow she didn't think it was her own feeble struggles which had stopped him in the end. Perhaps—she gave the thumbscrew of her unhappiness another painful twist—perhaps Rowena's shattered portrait had inadvertently entered Luke's mind, as Tanya doubted if her faint cry of protest had ever reached him at all.

It was after lunch when she met him on the stairs. She hadn't seen him earlier in the day and had allowed herself to be lulled into the belief that he would want to avoid her for some time. She stared at him, her eyes dazed as if by shock as he strode towards her, and because she was on her way down she couldn't even evade him by looking in the other direction. From every angle he could see her face and though she knew an urge to turn about and run, pride forbade her.

Her heart quaked as she thought he might make some reference to that period in his room which she would rather forget, but she wasn't sure that she didn't feel worse when he merely said, 'We're having guests tonight, Tanya. Think you can cope?'

What made him think it was her place to? She was supposed to be employed here, but he must know this for a joke as well as she. Faintly agitated and not a little perplexed, she asked dryly, 'Am I allowed to enquire who is coming—I mean if it's an Indian business man we must plan accordingly.'

Luke's eyes narrowed, going sharply to her pure profile which she managed to keep cool. She thought his revenge calculated when he replied smoothly, 'Sure. The Browns and Mrs Harrison.'

'Rowena!' Startled, Tanya's eyes clashed angrily with his. She had thought it would be his overseer, or someone flying in from Fiji. It hadn't occurred to her that it would be Rowena so soon, and not after last night.

'It's one way of making you look at me when I speak to you,' he said suavely. 'And it's Mrs Harrison to you.'

Tanya's hands clenched into tight balls. 'Of course, Mr Harrison.'

'I want you to wear something sweet and pretty—a dress to make you appear the attractive young girl you are. And you can leave off the sulky expression. I have no use for a girl that young.'

Later, as she changed for dinner, she couldn't stop wondering about his motives, because Luke Harrison was never a man to do anything merely as a whim. Why did he want her to look—what had he said, sweet and pretty? Was it to make Rowena look twice and feel jealous? It seemed he definitely had his ex-wife in mind. Hadn't he almost snapped her head off for calling her Rowena? On the stairs so much had trembled uncertainly on her lips, so much she had wanted desperately to say, yet he hadn't stayed a minute longer than necessary. He had simply smiled at her rather cruelly and almost brushed her out of his way.

The dress Tanya finally chose turned her, she decided derisively, into everything he demanded. It was white, young and of deceptively innocent cut. Belted tightly to a narrow waist, the wide skirt floated gently about her slender ankles to which she buckled the narrow straps of a pair of fragile silver sandals. The bodice was accordingly demure, the rounded neckline showing a mere glimpse of shadowed curves. She had no jewellery to wear with it, but this didn't seem to matter. It might only have drawn attention to her unhappiness to have worn a glittering ornament which found no answering sparkle in her eyes.

She wasn't happy, she didn't expect to be again, but at least her face in the mirror had a fine, clear outline all of its own. Her dress might be borrowed, but her features were not, neither was the burnished, tawny hair that swung heavily from a widow's peak. To her lips she applied the merest hint of lip gloss, otherwise leaving make-up off altogether. In spite of Luke's commands, she refused to give the impression that she was competing with any woman, least of all Rowena.

Like herself, Miss Logan had also been ordered to put in an appearance and, in a similar fashion, didn't seem to be too enthusiastic. Possibly fearing Luke's displeasure they didn't discuss it over tea, but Tanya sensed that Miss Logan was anxious. 'You'll see what Rowena looks like at last,' was all Elizabeth said as they went up to change.

When later Tanya went along to her room to collect her she felt suddenly that Miss Logan's worried thoughts were concentrated on herself more than any coming ordeal. There was something not wholly approving in her tired grey eyes as they rested contemplatively on Tanya's charming young face.

Tanya concluded that it might be that Miss Logan considered her selection of a dress not too appropriate for a paid companion, but she found it impossible to explain. It wasn't something she could easily put into words; Miss Logan might simply conclude she was making it up. Tanya's bitterness seemed to increase as Elizabeth took Toma's arm, apparently in preference to hers, to be helped downstairs. So much seemed to have gone wrong since she had given in to the insane desire to see the photograph of a woman whom only a short while later she was to meet anyway.

To Tanya's surprise Luke went to fetch his guests personally. Miss Logan said stiffly, 'Naturally the Browns don't drive after dark now, and Rowena has always been nervous of our island roads.'

'But they have servants?'

'Luke obviously wished to go himself.'

Tanya, who would dearly have loved a sherry or something long and cool in a glass to occupy her hands and bolster her up, was forced to await their arrival with a mouth so dry as to make her feel almost ill. It was an experience she never hoped to repeat.

The Browns entered first, followed closely by Luke with a slim, graceful woman on his arm. Tanya was duly introduced after Rowena had exchanged a few polite remarks with Miss Logan, whom she greeted with amusement as Logie.

On the face of it she seemed as much amused by Tanya. 'So this is your little nursemaid, Logie dear? Isn't it strange the tricks life plays. Now that you're old your position, so to speak, has been reversed.'

Tanya felt she hated Rowena immediately because of the cruelty of that, and didn't care if it showed. She saw Miss Logan tremble and went straight way to her side, giving, she supposed, some weight to Rowena's barbed observation.

Luke, solicitously, helped Rowena off with her beautiful fur cape, while Tanya discreetly squeezed Miss Logan's hand and wondered if it was mink and if he had bought it. The Browns began talking and it was a chance to study Rowena. She seemed much better looking than her photograph, as this hadn't shown the excellence of her reed-thin figure. Miss Logan said she was a year younger than Luke, but time must have dealt with her kindly as she would have passed for a lot less than thirty-five. Her mouth was the only feature to let her down, this being over-thin and narrow and combined occasionally with a coldness of expression to make the subject of her disapproval shiver.

Miss Logan, in fact, seemed nervous of Rowena, but the Browns appeared, on the other hand, to admire her, and from them Tanya gathered that Rowena was welcome to stay as long as she liked.

'I might stay a few more weeks,' Rowena assured the table in general during dinner. She smiled confidently. 'Luke misses me. Don't you, darling?'

'Naturally.' Luke spoke lazily and his glance was more

appreciative as it ran over her thin elegance than when it rested on Tanya.

Tanya felt hollow to the bottom of her stomach, but it was nothing to her discomfort when she heard herself retorting sweetly, 'Then it's a great pity you ever left, Mrs Harrison.'

As soon as she spoke Tanya's glance flew apprehensively to Luke's face. Why must her tongue always be running away with her? His narrowed eyes, meeting hers, promised she would suffer, although no one else might have guessed his momentary savageness from the returning blandness of his expression.

He smiled at Rowena and she returned his smile with great assurance. Rowena was not over-sensitive, she appeared to take most things at face value. 'That's something I intend putting right, Miss Willis.'

Having asked for all she seemed to have received, Tanya subsided in a flood of bleak despair. Her face went pale and she remained silent after that, scarcely trusting herself to speak again. Luke stared at her from time to time but didn't address her, and Tanya noticed that she and Miss Logan seemed the only ones entirely satisfied with their evening.

They were loading copra next day and Tanya was eager to find out if she knew any of the boats which came for it. She had got to know many of the captains when living on Karowi and was curious to see who would be there. Most of the copra boats had coloured captains who spoke the most perfect English, and she had always found them perfect gentlemen as well. Usually big and with a heart to match, nothing had been too much bother and they were polite in the extreme. Many a time they had gone out of their way to call at Karowi with a parcel of food, knowing they could never hope to be properly compensated.

There was always a spare jeep at Luke's house and this morning was no exception. Toma promised to look after Elizabeth for a while and, risking Luke's wrath, Tanya flung on a pair of shorts and brief top and drove down to the village. The last boat was in, the loading almost completed, but she could see nothing of the captain. One of the islanders told her he was in the office with the boss. With the smell of dried copra so heavy on the air Tanya wasn't keen to linger, so she turned and went in that direction. Apparently if she wanted to see the captain she must see Luke too; there seemed nothing else for it. She might somehow contrive to get a word with the captain, if she knew him, alone.

To her delight the first person she saw on opening the office door was Captain James, whom she knew well. Her pleasure was short-lived, however, when, looking past him, she saw Rowena. Luke was there, as she had expected, and so was Jules Malou, his overseer. They were all having drinks and Rowena sat with her hand on Luke's bare arm, laughing up into his face, as if enjoying a shared joke. That Rowena was here at all seemed to emphasise something intimate in the atmosphere and instinctively Tanya shrank back, or would have done if Captain James hadn't caught sight of her and with a great whoop snatched her up.

'Well, for landsake, child!' he roared, his weatherbeaten old face crinkling. 'I never thought to catch sight of you again! You're a sight for sore eyes.'

'I hoped I might find you here,' she cried recklessly, because this was her most favourite captain. Then she bit her lip as he set her happily down. Now Luke would imagine she had come with every intention of bribing Captain James to help her escape when this had really been far from her mind. At least—she bit her lip some more— she had thought of making one or two tentative enquiries, but only if it was someone she knew.

Deliberately she smiled brilliantly at the stalwart captain, somehow knowing it wouldn't please Luke. Luke, his brow black as it had been for days when turned in Tanya's direction, shook off Rowena's arm none too gently. Interposing himself between Tanya and the beaming captain, he looked coldly at the slender, coltish length of her bare legs.

'Is something wrong at the house?' he asked crisply, infuriating her with the clear indication that unless there was she shouldn't be here.

'Nothing's the matter, Mr Harrison,' she replied, averting her eyes. 'I came to see Captain James, not you.'

'Do you know Miss Willis?' Rowena was there, her arm slipping naturally through Luke's again, as if she couldn't bear not to be near him.

'Of course I do.' Tanya noticed Captain James sobered a little as he glanced obliquely at Rowena. 'Didn't Miss Tanya come to live on Karowi with her father, poor man? She's a real fine little girl, is Miss Tanya.'

Tanya tried to smile appreciatively, but Rowena's presence had an enervating effect, and the sarcastic quirk to Luke's mouth didn't help either. Captain James, although it seemed apparent he didn't care too much for Rowena, chose not to be disturbed by her and went on to ask Tanya what were her plans for the future—what was she doing now?

'Working for my husband,' Rowena smiled, and when James looked curious, entirely unselfconsciously she added, 'I still think of him as this. Old habits die hard and I know he doesn't mind, do you, darling?'

This time Tanya did look at Luke and felt slightly sick when he smiled back at Rowena, as if he agreed with her. What a positive fool she had been! All her strivings, her naïve attempts to save him and Miss Logan, had been futile. It was quite obvious that he was more than willing to meet Rowena half way. All Tanya knew was left to do now was show him she didn't care.

He even had the nerve, while everyone watched, to put a gentle arm around Rowena's waist. 'I must go, my dear. I'll see Tanya back to the house.'

'Isn't she supposed to be working?' Rowena frowned.

'This is why she's going back to the house,' he said curtly. 'I'm afraid her powwow with Captain James must keep till another day.'

But by a small twist of fate Tanya did manage a quick word with her friend, in spite of Luke's grim surveillance.

One of the islanders, loading the copra, hurt himself and Luke went to see that it wasn't serious.

Captain James, as if realising every second counted, spoke to Tanya in swift undertones. 'If ever you need me, child, just get me word. I'll be back, anyway, in about two months' time and will see you then.'

Luke returned. The man had only suffered a scrape and fright; Jules could cope with it. Rowena, who had trailed to the door, decided she would come back to the house with Luke and Tanya for coffee.

'I'll still have plenty of time to join the Browns for lunch,' she smiled, as Tanya said goodbye to Captain James.

Over coffee, which Luke demanded that Tanya stay to pour out, Tanya managed to keep her mind blank, so that no new hurt could penetrate to swell the pain already there. Rowena acted strangely, seemingly preoccupied, casting an occasional contemplative glance at Tanya although she smiled enough at Luke.

When he was called to the office for a few minutes, Rowena stretched languidly, looking not altogether displeased by the interruption. She even smiled at Tanya, 'Luke has promised to take me to your island tomorrow. He thinks it will be fun. Why don't you come along?'

Tanya replaced her coffee cup abruptly in its saucer, feeling suddenly cold. So this was how Luke regarded Karowi! She didn't want to go there again, not so soon, memories were still too painful. Luke and Rowena would undoubtedly find it amusing, as it could be, she supposed, to look around a place where other people had lived. Rowena would poke around everywhere with smart exclamations—she was that kind of woman. She would turn it to her own advantage, poke discreet fun until Tanya knew she would feel awful. Maybe this was why she had asked her along? She wondered miserably how Luke could have agreed to such a thing. Was it that he hoped to derive a subtle revenge because he considered she had made a fool of him the other night in his bedroom, by giving promises she hadn't been able to fulfil?

She was about to refuse Rowena's mysterious invitation when Luke came back and Rowena cut in quickly, 'Tanya would like to visit her old home, Luke. I expect we could do with someone to make tea.'

Luke glanced sharply towards Tanya. He didn't seem any too pleased with the idea. He must want Rowena to himself, probably to propose to her again, Tanya thought, with a mirthless inner giggle. She didn't see how Rowena could pass up such an opportunity; she must be quite confident it would come again. Or—Tanya's heart slowed to a dull thud—it could be that Luke had already made his intentions clear. Certainly the satisfied expression on Rowena's face suggested this might be so.

'I think Tanya would be better here,' Luke said curtly.

'I wouldn't!' Something about the way he spoke stung Tanya to this surprising reply, one which puzzled Luke, she suspected, as much as herself. It wasn't that she wanted to go at all, but she felt a fierce surge of protectiveness towards the small island. It would be impossible to explain logically, but she knew she must accept Rowena's offer even if it didn't suit Luke's plans.

Amazingly, the fact that Luke seemed far from enthusiastic only appeared to make Rowena more determined that Tanya should accompany them. When Luke continued to stare grimly at a white-faced Tanya, and asked what she proposed to do with Elizabeth if they were all away, Rowena immediately suggested that the Browns should come and look after her for the day.

'We won't be gone that long, Luke, and Logie has always got on with Edna. Actually I think you're slightly exaggerating Logie's condition. She always had to be humoured, I remember. Her one ambition was to have the nursery filled with screaming children.'

When Luke made no reply other than to nod expressionlessly, Rowena rounded off brightly, 'I'll bring the Browns over after breakfast. We'll probably be back and gone long before dinner.' She smiled brilliantly, so self-effacing that

Tanya couldn't help wondering uncharitably just what she was up to.

It was an effort to get up next morning and for long minutes after she woke Tanya lay still, wishing she didn't have to. She could have got out of going to the island—and why she should subject herself to the torture of watching Luke with the woman he loved, she didn't know! After the episode in his room she found herself scarcely able to look him straight in the face, and it seemed unfair that he hadn't been affected by it at all. Having to spend a whole day with him might be more than she could stand.

When at last she dressed and went down to breakfast it was still early and she hoped to be finished before Luke came in from the plantation for his. It was mortifying to find him already there.

He eyed Tanya's pale face grimly. 'If I didn't know better I'd say the air around here didn't agree with you. As it is I can only conclude it's something else that's getting beneath that delightful skin of yours.'

'Not you, at any rate,' she flashed back untruthfully, a pounding pulse arousing a faint bravado, slightly foreign to her nature. With fumbling fingers she pulled out a chair.

Luke picked up the coffee pot and poured two cups, his mouth clamping impatiently. 'Sit down and have something to eat and stop playing the offended party. That must be my prerogative, I'm thinking.'

She flushed, hating him as vivid colour stained her smooth cheeks. 'At least you aren't this morning,' she couldn't resist pointing out.

'Maybe,' he taunted, his eyes catching and holding hers in a vice, 'I can handle my grievances better than you, but that's not to say they aren't still there.'

Her breath caught and she slumped in her chair, wrenching her widening gaze to the cream lace table mats which wavered in the polished surface. She had asked for that! 'Won't Mrs Harrison be coming?' she faltered. 'Oughtn't we to wait?'

The hard line of his jaw relaxed a little, as if even the sound of Rowena's name improved his temper. 'She won't be here yet awhile,' he replied, briefly. His eyes went to Tanya's waist as she pulled herself up straighter. 'You want a tuck,' he grinned.

'They did fit last week,' she replied absently, her hand moving carelessly to the belt of her brief shorts, 'and they seem the most sensible thing for island-hopping.'

He sighed, taking in the strain around her young mouth which she was doing her best to hide, 'Tanya,' he began, 'you're losing weight and I won't have you worried. You don't have to ...' Whatever was coming next was cut off short as Rowena burst in, throwing the rattan screen presumptuously aside. Edna Brown fluttered smilingly behind her.

'I'm early, Luke,' she said lightly, as if only pandering to his slightly raised brows, not because she thought an explanation necessary. 'Edna and John have friends flying in later, unexpectedly, which means, of course, we shall have to be back earlier. John has promised to hold the fort, but we can't impose too much on his good nature.'

As Luke's launch skimmed swiftly over the water, the sky above them was blue, the sun golden, tipping every lazy wave with a glittering gold dust. Not a cloud flecked the sky and a faint breeze died as the sun rose higher; it was going to be a beautiful day. Or it might have been, Tanya reflected wistfully, if Rowena hadn't been here and they'd been on their way to any other place but Karowi.

The boat gathered speed, cutting cleanly through the crystal waters, and her eyes gravitated towards Luke's dark head at the helm. What would his life become if he married Rowena again? Rowena's comments yesterday about the nursery didn't seem to indicate a change of mind about some things. She seemed to have forgotten what it must have been like for a man like Luke Harrison to be deprived of the family he wanted. Yet to have lived on his own during the years since he had let her go seemed to prove he had discovered that Rowena was of more importance than children. It certainly appeared that Rowena had de-

cided it was like this. Unless, of course, it was she who had
changed and was now willing to fill the empty nursery as
soon as she regained her legal status.

Too soon, it seemed, Karowi rose from the sea, its
girdling reefs flashing white with leaping surf, and it surprised Tanya the fuss Rowena made when she got wet getting through them.

'We'd have been wiser to have chosen one of the larger
islands,' Luke grunted, holding Tanya's arm, not noticeably
sympathetic with Rowena in view of her bedraggled appearance. Yet, in spite of her wet hair and slightly dripping
mascara, Rowena still managed to look attractive, if a little
nearer her real age.

Luke, after scanning Tanya's damp cheeks narrowly, let
go of her arm and removed his shirt, draping it scarf-like
across his powerful shoulders. He looked tall and virile and
made Tanya's pulse miss a beat and her face colour
sensuously even to look at him. Rowena, on the other hand,
merely averted her fastidious gaze, as if his semi-nakedness
offended her. Tanya knew Luke noticed their differing reactions with dry amusement and disliked him intensely.

Tui was there to meet them as Tanya had hoped he
would be, and she almost clung to his outstretched hands,
tears clinging unashamedly to her long lashes. He greeted
her gravely along with the other two and insisted they go
to his village. On the islands the natives made use of any
excuse to have a feast, and today was no exception. One was
already being prepared, although, as Tui pointed out, they
had had very little warning. 'We only know you come when
you set out.'

While Tanya sighed and wondered how on earth the
islanders knew these things without any normal means of
communication, Tui welcomed Rowena formally. This was
something else that puzzled Tanya—that the people both
here and on Luke's island seemed to regard Rowena coolly.
Was it because they considered she had let the big boss
down and were being cautious?

In the small village to which Tui escorted them, they

ate young pig with other cooked meat, vegetables and fish. It had all been cooked in a hole in the ground, where a pile of firewood had been burning for some time to heat the stones in the bottom. Everything was then wrapped in leaves from a nearby tree, a thicker layer of leaves covering the food before earth was smoothed on top to prevent the steam from escaping. It all tasted delicious, and Tanya, who had participated in such feasts before, found she was hungry. Rowena left almost everything she was offered, declaring decidedly that she was not.

Afterwards Rowena, not troubling to hide her boredom, demanded to see where Tanya had lived. Tui and his wife returned to the beach with them, remaining by Tanya's side while Rowena explored the burnt-out ruins of the cabin. Luke strolled with her, obviously answering numerous questions, as Tanya watched with unhappy eyes.

A few minutes later she became aware that Tui was regarding her with an anxiously grave expression. 'I hope the little missy happy now?' he said soberly.

'Mr Harrison is very kind ...' It wasn't a direct reply, but she felt reluctant to confess to the old islander that far from being happy she was almost in despair.

Tui looked at her, his eyes cloud-cool, an expression she didn't wholly understand, 'You must not behave foolishly, little missy,' he said in a low voice no one else could have overheard. 'If you ever need help come back here. We will look after you. Whatever mistake you make we remember you are good and that you loved us.'

Why, thought Tanya, with a heavy heart as they sailed away, did everyone appear to imagine she would need help? Anyone might need help at some time or other, but there was something different here, she was sure. It was like a bad omen, the way Captain James and now the islanders seemed to believe she was in some kind of self-afflicted peril. Unconsciously she shuddered, and it was like someone walking over her grave.

CHAPTER EIGHT

It puzzled Tanya, afterwards, as to why Rowena had been so keen for her to go to Karowi. She had gone with a kind of faint dread, half expecting something terrible to happen, and when it didn't she came to the reluctant conclusion that Rowena had merely set out to uprate her personal image with Luke by proving she could be very generously disposed to those less fortunate than herself. Reviewing the day, Tanya didn't think anyone could have been more charming.

The next day passed with Tanya seeing very little of Luke. She didn't think he was quite so busy on the plantation, and concluded that he must be entertaining Rowena while the Browns had other visitors.

Surprisingly, Tanya's visit to the island hadn't renewed her former pain. In fact, now, she seemed to feel a whole lot better about her father than she had done since his death. Incredibly she could even contemplate going over his rejected manuscripts with a mixture of pride and determination, rather than her former unhappy reluctance.

If she was really sorry about one thing it was that Miss Logan appeared to have suffered a minor setback while they had been away. Tanya couldn't understand it as Miss Logan had been quite content to stay with Edna Brown, who had assured them, when they returned, that everything had gone well. Whatever had upset her she was quieter and had little to say. She wouldn't reply when Tanya asked her if anything was wrong. It was Miss Logan's refusal to answer this specific question that bothered Tanya. She was so worried that she decided, with some trepidation, to wait up and see if she could catch Luke as he came in.

It was a difficult decision to make as she had no wish to have him think she was deliberately waylaying him, but he could be gone before she was down in the morning and if anything did happen to be wrong with Elizabeth he could rightly accuse her of neglect.

She sat in the lounge until almost eleven waiting for him. He had not been in for dinner and Miss Logan had gone early to bed, with Toma in charge. Feeling oddly deserted and lonely, Tanya was about to ring for more coffee when she suddenly realised she had ordered two lots since dinner and scarcely drank any of it. Anyway, Dino would probably have retired for the night and she didn't want to look too cosy when Luke arrived.

Because her mind seemed to be going around in crazy circles, she gave a sigh of relief when she heard him eventually come in. About to give him up, she had her hand on the lounge door when she heard him dismiss Dino after telling him curtly he wanted no refreshments. She waited until Dino's quick footsteps faded before she let Luke know she was there.

'Could I have a word with you, please?'

She spoke to his broad back and he swung around sharply. 'Still up? Dino didn't mention it.' He strode towards her with a frown, his narrowed glance taking in her slim young figure, graceful in flowered cotton. While he didn't smile he didn't look particularly displeased to see her standing there, for which, she supposed, she should be grateful.

'Yes.' She caught her lips as she so often did when he was near. It seemed an instinctive reaction she couldn't break and her breathing played its usual tricks. Luke might be ruthless, heartless, but to be near him was to realise how much she was coming to love him. How much, in spite of everything, she longed for his tenderness. She didn't think he had just come from Rowena as he still wore the clothes he used for work and his tough khaki shirt was crumpled and she could smell the sweaty heat from his body.

He mistook her backward shrinking for repulsion, not realising she fought a momentary urge to throw herself into his arms, to enquire gently if he had had a heavy day.

'You don't have to wrinkle your fastidious little nose at
me,' he sneered, as she quickly lowered her nervous blue
eyes. 'I've been working and may not be too nice to be
near, but you might not be able to be choosy much longer.
You might indeed be glad of me, sweat and all!'

It wasn't a good start. In her face was a unhappy fore-
boding that this wasn't to be as simple as she'd thought. She
felt mortified, as if he had insulted her, and she clenched
her trembling hands stiffly so he wouldn't guess how his
caustic comments hurt.

'I never have any objection to honest sweat,' she stammered, her words erupting wildly as she strove too hard to
assure him. She must sound as if she was addressing a lower
servant! She tried to continue more calmly. 'I wanted to
see you, but it will only take a minute. I won't keep you.'
For all her uncertainty she felt extraordinarily glad he
hadn't been with Rowena.

His eyes mocked her prim little request. 'As I happen to
want a word with you too, and what I have to say might
take longer than your minute, I suggest we may as well go
back to the lounge, discuss our business in comfort.'

Courteously he held the door for her to pass, then closed
it again firmly behind him, taking no notice of the flicker of
near hostility in her eyes. She expected a lecture—wasn't he
always ticking her off about something? She should be
getting used to his high-handed manner, but tonight she
felt almost too strung up to cope.

'Sit down, Tanya. You look about to drop in any case.'
He looked weary himself, the harsh lines about his mouth
not encouraging, but she groped for a chair, glad for once to
take his advice.

'You go first,' he ordered, going to the sideboard and
pouring himself half a tumbler of whisky. 'Mine,' he added
dryly, 'will keep a few minutes longer.'

That sounded dangerously potential somehow. It almost
put her off her stride, if she had ever been on it. 'It's about
Miss Logan,' she began, her expression changing to one of

sudden urgency, 'I don't think she's quite herself. She's been quiet all day.'

Luke's eyes rested grimly on Tanya's face. 'She usually talks a lot now, doesn't she?'

If Tanya had stopped to think about it she might almost have said he was stalling for time. 'Yes, but not today,' she repeated. 'Some,' she hesitated ruefully, 'might be glad of a lull, but after the island I find I enjoy her chatter. Anyway, I found this new silence much more disturbing.'

Luke poured himself another drink, another stiff one, she noticed with surprise, as he usually relied on his own cast-iron equilibrium. Then there was the shock of his voice again, hard and bracing. 'You might find what I have to say disturbs you more. You see, I happen to know the reason for Elizabeth's present attitude, the silence she directs only towards yourself.'

'You do?' Tanya felt perplexed, noting his emphasis on the last word. 'She does talk to Toma. This is what hurts as I'm sure I haven't done anything, at least not that I know of, to worry her. If I thought I had . . .'

'Listen to me, Tanya,' he interrupted abruptly. 'You feel puzzled, yet you've lived on these islands long enough to realise that when you spent a night in my room it would have repercussions.'

For dazed moments Tanya stared at him while shock flared uncontrollably through her and some fearful emotion clutched at her throat. Her blue eyes darkened to near black. 'No one could have known,' her voice trailed off to a disbelieving whisper, 'unless you told someone?'

'You know you're wrong there, on both counts,' his tone was clipped. 'The islanders, the natives of these lands, know of such things without being told, especially if they're curious about someone, as they are about you. You might say they can sense events as though they were eye-witnesses. Call it black magic or whatever you like. Personally I always refer to it as white because in most cases it is harmless. From the air they appear, on occasion, to be able to conjure the most incredible truths. How, for instance, do they get messages from one isolated island to another? Tui knew we were coming yesterday—and don't ask me for a logical explanation.'

Tanya could do no more than stare at him while attempting to pull herself together. How many knew? she wondered. Was this why Captain James and Tui had both offered refuge with such sad expressions on their faces? As if they already contemplated her ruin and felt sorry for her? It was amazing how enlightened one became with patience! 'So what?' she said dully, at last. 'I suppose I'm now branded a scarlet woman?'

He looked as if he might lay brutal hands on her, as he returned her blank stare grimly. 'Tanya! If you're going to be flippant, you might get more than you bargain for.'

She shrank visibly from the near anger in his voice. 'I'm sorry,' she muttered, 'I expect Rowena won't like it.'

'You can leave Rowena out of this. At least she would have had more sense than to place herself in such a compromising situation.'

That hurt. Tanya tried again. 'There seems to be only one solution—I must go. But surely,' she felt so near tears she was forced to take a deep breath, 'surely if they knew I was in your bedroom that night they must have known nothing took place, and that I've never been there since?'

'These people aren't like this. Once a fact is established they don't follow it up morbidly, like a popular radio series.'

'Who told Miss Logan?' Tanya's voice was bitter. 'I expect this is why she's gone all cold on me?'

'Toma.'

'And ...?'

'Yes, Elizabeth tackled me. She's naturally in rather a state, but will get over it when we put things right.'

'Put things right?' Tanya, by this time aware of Miss Logan's rigidly held views, couldn't see how this could be achieved. By her own unthinking act she had blotted her own copybook good and proper—or should it be improper! Pressing a nervous hand against her mouth, Tanya strove to keep back hysterical tears. 'We could never put things right,' she mumbled, through shaking fingers.

'We can.' Luke, ignoring her distress, was coolly master of the situation, a mockery reflecting in his voice if not his eyes as they rested on Tanya's graceful head, the silky hair, thick and tawny against her sharp pallor. 'We'll get married,' he said slowly, so she might take it all in, 'just as soon as I can arrange it.'

'Married!' Tanya was on her feet, her paleness a bright, flamy red.

'You heard.'

This, she thought wildly, must be something unique in the way of proposals! The way he framed it, the almost insulting hardness of his eyes and voice in which she could detect not one note of tenderness. He must be joking, of course. 'You can't be contemplating sacrificing yourself just to save my good name. Once I'm away from here no one will know. Not that there's anything to know anyway,' she choked.

'You and I know this, but others don't, and it's the bad rumour which always follows people. I'm not going to pretend to make too much of it, but given certain circumstances your life could be hell. Whereas, once you're married to me, it would immediately be forgotten.'

'And you, what would you gain?' she cried, panic beginning to strike at her wildly.

'The people here, my people, would no longer look on me as a kind of monster, bent on seducing young girls. I would get a wife and Elizabeth would see the old nurseries weren't empty any more, when she comes to visit.'

'Oh!' Her slim body became rigid yet felt strangely hot, while the pink in her cheeks deepened. The implications of that were all too clear, but at least he was frank! She wouldn't say honest, this was a virtue she didn't attribute to him, not now. He must have known how the minds of his islanders worked, and if he had carried her straight back to his room that night surely no one would have been any the wiser. He must be a remarkable fiend; it didn't seem as if he had even tried to explain the true story to Elizabeth. And there was still his ex-wife. 'I thought you intended marrying Rowena again?' she said faintly, and quite truthfully.

He smiled, if a little grimly. 'It might be wiser to stop thinking, Tanya. Just as I'm going to do, for a while.'

What did he mean? Would she ever understand this enigmatical man, supposing she was married to him a hundred years? Did he still love Rowena but was afraid to put much faith into her apparent change of heart? Men, it seemed, could be impulsive, yet on the other hand, mysteriously cautious.

Tanya tried to look at him squarely but failed dismally, her breath quivering in the quiet room. Luke had asked her to marry him, and if she did it would be because she loved him too much to let him go, not for any other reason, although she must pretend. She did her best to conceal her own intense feelings. 'What if I refuse?'

He knew she was talking of his proposal. 'Let me put it this way,' he stared down into the eyes which wavered apprehensively under his, 'you owe me quite a lot. Now that you're relying heavily on me to restore your good name you appear to be deeper in my debt than ever. To marry me and try to make amends would seem the only course left open to you. I don't see how you can refuse. Remember, too, to think of me. A young bride can be a trial as well as a pleasure.'

'Luke . . .'

'Listen to me, Tanya.' Suddenly, to her surprise, he was gripping her arms, drawing her to him, some of his hardness of manner dispersing as he pulled her quite gently against him. 'There'll be compensations, you know. I think, to begin with, it's an advantage that we understand each other. You need looking after and a good home. I want a wife who won't expect to get her own way in everything.'

'Supposing I do? I might try.' The urge to rest her tired head against his shoulder was almost too much, and it was only comfort she was seeking for the weariness which seemed to be attacking her very bones. Yet so near him she felt herself quiver and tautened, wondering how far he intended to go. Did he imagine she was full of unexplored passion, or, on the other hand, did he realise the depth of her inexperience?

His eyes narrowed, but only slightly, as he heard her faint defiance. 'I imagine, like most women, you'll try at some time or another, but I refuse to spoil you.'

She felt a coldness wash over her. 'You'll find it easy to chastise a wife you don't love.'

'It's perhaps better that there's no love between us,' he hesitated fractionally. 'Once I married, thinking myself in love, and it was a disaster.'

She heard the harsh bleakness returning to his tones and her heart shuddered in her breast as she considered his young devotion. He was still a young man, but much older than he had been then. No boy now to be dictated to by a pair of appealing feminine eyes, but he seemed also to have lost much of youth's spontaneous joy. Had Rowena done this to him?

As if he, too, sensed Rowena's unseen presence between them, he thrust Tanya suddenly from him, as if regretting his momentary tenderness. Tanya, who for all her tiredness had felt her blood stir warmly to be so near him, felt chilled. What was the use of longing for kisses which he would never give voluntarily? Kisses of passion, maybe, when it suited him, but nothing else. Not even these when he was brooding over Rowena. Yet what else could she expect when he no more than vaguely liked her and her own love was still too vulnerable to be able to influence him in any way?

He picked up his empty glass, turning as if to fill it, then, apparently changing his mind, set it down again. His hardening glance, as it swung back to her fraught white face, suggested more clearly than words that he considered he was putting himself to a great deal of trouble. 'We'll tell Elizabeth in the morning. Once something's decided it's better acted on right away. Two days later, at the most, we fly to Fiji and get married.'

'So soon!' He might have been making a business arrangement. It didn't seem possible. Tanya wasn't ready for this step yet. In a few weeks' time, perhaps ... Her great blue eyes fixed imploringly on his cold face. 'I don't see any reason why we should rush into this, Luke. So long as Elizabeth knows we're to be married this should put everything right.'

'We aren't rushing into anything, Tanya,' his voice was slow and deliberate as if to emphasise his point. 'The sooner we get it over the better. It might have been different if it had been a normal engagement, but we aren't exactly a moonstruck couple. Nor do we have to start from rock bottom. We have a house, a settled home on the island, and I have enough money to keep you in comfort.'

'So what more could a girl want?' she whispered, struck to audible fury. 'It amazes me that you haven't a line of possible candidates lined up, just waiting for Mr Harrison Almighty to confer the honour of his name. In my case the right word must be protection, and I suppose you expect me to salaam myself prostrate before you!'

His green eyes had flames at the back of them and his gentleness of a moment ago had gone. In its place was the hard cynicism with which she was all too familiar. 'Behave yourself, Tanya, or I might forget to be what you call reasonable and treat you as I would a spoilt child. Before we get married you'd better decide if you want to be dealt with as one. There's another side to you that I'm entirely aware of, one which I might not ignore.'

She felt a fire kindling, like an unholy agreement within her. He seemed to know her inside out, or he knew what he had done to her. She hadn't come to terms herself with how she reacted in his arms, and it didn't help that he seemed able to weigh and assess so perfectly. She flung out her slender hands tautly. 'You have the superior strength.'

'I hope so!' His eyes glittered. 'You need a strong guiding hand. One day, when you realise it and feel grateful, you might let me know. In the meantime, no more dramatics. They may suit you, with your half wild little airs, but they definitely don't suit me. I've had quite a day, one way and another.'

Tanya's heavy lashes fluttered as she stared at him, apprehension joining fearfully with exhaustion and a growing bewilderment. Everything was piling up on her, and although Luke declared he was tired, too, she wished she had a half of his cool authority. He had a hard, offhand look about him, like a man holding himself in check, making allowances for her young uncertainties which offended his supreme arrogance. She knew she had to make one last try, even when he so clearly desired her out of his sight so he could enjoy a last drink in peace. That she was outstaying her welcome was obvious from his tight-lipped regard. There was to be no engagement kiss, no goodnight one, either. Not, Tanya assured herself hurriedly, that she expected such a thing!

She drew a breath guardedly. 'Do we really have to rush into anything, Luke? Surely a period of engagement would cause less talk than a hurried marriage? In fact this might not be necessary, as people will forget.' She forgot that only a few nights ago she had offered herself ingloriously and would have maybe welcomed marriage then.

'If it's only talk you're worried about,' he shrugged, 'then I'd advise you to forget it. I believe to sit around looking at each other for weeks would only put an interminable strain on the situation. On us, if you like, and you've had enough of that.'

'But in a way we hardly know each other.'

He laughed, as if he could actually see the tremble that went all over her body when he looked at her. 'You know me better than you're going to know any other man.'

'That's just it. I haven't known other men.' Was it a surge of terror that drove her on? 'I—I somehow can't envisage living with a man. I mean—not ...'

'God, child,' there was a hard, mocking quality to his voice that hurt her, 'I'm not a brute altogether, although there are times when you seem capable of arousing violence in me. Why do you think I'm proposing to take you to Fiji?

A week or two away and the islanders will have lost interest. They won't wonder whether you're properly my wife or
not.'

'But when we come back here?' She couldn't leave it,
torn as she was between fear of him and a desire, as yet
partly unformed, to belong to him completely. Wasn't it the
height of folly to wonder what it would be like to have him
say he wanted her, that one day, one night soon ...

'I've told you, Tanya, I'm not longer a callow youth to
force myself where I know I'm not wanted.'

His sensuous mouth twisted and she suspected she had
handled it badly in being so persistent. Her voice con-
sequently faltered. 'You kissed me—you ...'

'Go to bed, my dear. It's a subject better left alone. I
refuse to discuss it to the bitter end, if this is what you're
bent on. I'm not immune to a pretty face, an enticing
virginal body, so be comforted, or otherwise, that I have my
weaknesses, but a man's not a man until he's learnt a
measure of control. I can find plenty to keep me occupied
elsewhere.'

As Tanya rushed blindly upstairs she wondered if he
meant Rowena.

Elizabeth was delighted with the news of their marriage.
'I know you'll be very happy, dear,' she beamed at Tanya,
her former disapproving silence apparently forgotten.
'You've got yourself a fine man.'

'Spare my blushes,' Luke murmured, without batting an
eyelid.

'Now I shall be able to retire happily.'

'We'd love to have you back any time,' said Tanya,
knowing, with humiliation, that it was she who blushed, not
Luke.

Luke went out, naturally having a lot of arranging to
do. He was emphatic, this morning, that they would leave
for Fiji next day, so he was going to be busy. Tanya didn't
realise how busy.

Over lunch he told her the Browns were coming to stay
with Elizabeth while they were away. When Tanya asked

hesitantly about their visitors he said they were flying out tomorrow in any case and Rowena would be with them.

Tanya should have been warned by the positive surge of relief that hit her. This seemed too good to be true. 'I'm glad, Luke.' He was not to know exactly what she was glad about, but he seemed to like the illuminating quality of her smile.

'I'm glad too.' He looked at her keenly as he rose to leave. 'Pleased that you're pleased about something anyway,' he quipped dryly.

Was it for Elizabeth's benefit that he pulled Tanya suddenly against him and kissed her, his hard mouth warm and searching on her soft one? He was gone before she could collect herself, but she was left with the surprising comfort that he maybe did like her a little.

While Elizabeth rested she spent part of the afternoon packing a few essentials. She didn't intend taking a lot. It wasn't that she minded so much wearing another girl's clothes, it was just that she didn't care to be married in them. It wasn't on, so far as she was concerned, to ask Luke for money to buy some of her own. He noticed what women wore, which seemed to prove all too clearly that he was aware of the situation but had no intention of putting himself out over it. If she arrived to be married in a pair of old jeans he might only raise an eyebrow, so why worry that she hadn't a white dress?

Even to pack a few things was exhausting, especially as she had not slept much the previous night. It was no wonder, recalling the way she had tossed and turned in it, that her bed looked less inviting than the sea. Grabbing her bikini, she ran down to the beach and lost herself for a blissful hour in the blue, mind-stopping water. She swam until she was nearly exhausted, then slept a while on the warm sand beneath her favourite palm.

Rowena woke her. Tanya felt sure someone dug brutally at her soft side with a vengeful toe, but when she sat up with a gasp Rowena was standing several yards from her.

'I've just come to say goodbye,' Rowena said smoothly. 'Dino told me where you were.'

'I see.' Tanya found it impossible to say she was sorry. There was a short silence, Rowena imposing it, knowing her effect on the other girl. 'I'll be back, you know.'

'Of course.'

Rowena moved a step nearer. 'You don't have to sit there mouthing polite little platitudes at me! Someone should have warned Luke the lengths a girl like you is prepared to go to get her own way!'

'Luke has a mind of his own.' Carefully Tanya brushed slim hands down her sand-hazed legs. What exactly was Rowena getting at?

'There's only one way a man's mind can work when he finds a girl like you in his bed. Luke always did the honourable thing, although I've told him this time he's going too far.'

'Luke told you—this?'

'You don't have to look shocked,' Rowena's dark eyes flashed vindictively. 'He's been telling me things a long time now.'

'But you're divorced.'

'Old habits die hard.' Rowena's laughter was brittle but convincing. 'I'm not perhaps flattering myself, but I am being honest when I say he values his freedom. An affair, yes, but nothing more tying. It's really a bit of a joke that he's been outwitted by a nondescript girl scarcely out of her teens!'

Shock showed on Tanya's face in a terrible pallor. Had they laughed or cursed her while Luke tried to explain? Maybe, as compensation, Luke had held Rowena in his arms and caressed her. Tanya hated him, her wildly passionate nature flaring in indignation as she turned her betraying eyes away from Rowena's contemptuous ones until she regained control. 'Elizabeth will wonder where I've got to,' she said tersely, getting to her feet.

'So it's Elizabeth now! Well, I won't say you're not a fast worker.'

'You didn't want him yourself, yet you hate the idea of anyone else ...' Tanya paused apprehensively, having no experience to buffer her silent rage with discretion. 'I've no patience with women who can't wait to be rid of a man and then do their utmost to get him back.'

'And I might have succeeded. You don't have to marry him, dear.'

'Nor do I have to stay here listening to you!' If she had stopped to consider Tanya could never have got that out. It sounded less than polite, but expressed the way she was feeling. Rowena's vindictiveness was hard to bear, but not as bad as her wheedling tones, especially when her last sentence contained more or less the same words Tanya had spoken to Luke herself. She turned, not giving Rowena another chance to offer more advice, flying back to the house as if the devil himself was after her.

She and Luke were married in Fiji three days later, and Tanya, almost exhausted by weeks of strain, was white beneath her tan but oddly relieved. Nothing much worse could happen, she was convinced. Nothing much worse than that which had taken place before they left the island, when she had accused Luke of confiding unforgivably in Rowena.

'What the hell are you on about now?' he asked grimly, the harsh lines around his mouth not encouraging.

Tanya concluded bitterly that they were there because of Rowena. 'You told Rowena that I'd been in your room.'

'No, Tanya, I did not. You'd have to be a fool to believe it.'

She shrank from the flaming anger in his eyes which curiously belied his cool tones. 'She sounded convincing,' she defended herself uncertainly.

'Convincing someone as naïve as you wouldn't be a major operation! As it is I don't give a damn what you believe. I'll tell you this and leave you to make of it what you like. Rowena is leaving the island and won't be coming back. There could be other women, of course, and you could be in danger of wearing yourself out, being suspicious of every one of them.'

The tenderness had gone, if it had been there at all when he had kissed her after lunch. Most definitely if there had been a glimmer of it it had merely been for Elizabeth's sake, as she had suspected. Momentarily, as he left her, the unhappiness she felt was reflected in her eyes as they met his, but he had neither stopped nor expressed a word of regret for having spoken so savagely and on such a subject to his young bride-to-be.

They flew to Viti Levu, the largest island in the Fiji group, and stayed the first night in Suva, the capital, where they were married next day. They spent what Tanya supposed would be regarded as their honeymoon in a luxury hotel many miles along the coast.

'I'm sorry this isn't Australia.' Luke's voice was clipped as he came to her room to see if she was dressed for dinner. 'One day I'll take you there to meet my family, or what's left of it—when you're good and ready.'

Tanya made a big thing of brushing her hair. It was smooth and glossy and thick, a little damp at the temples from perspiration. She didn't realise how the nape of her neck looked soft and vulnerable as she raised the hair from it, fashioning it in a cooler loop at the back of her small, perfect head. He wouldn't want to take her to Australia just now, when his family might guess their marriage was scarcely the result of two people being in love. She didn't reply as there seemed nothing she could say. Not while he towered above her looking sophisticated and supremely handsome in his dark dinner jacket. They had a suite of rooms and he had taken the smaller of the two bedrooms, but he wandered casually into hers, appearing much more comfortable than she felt.

'I like you in that shade of blue.' He was studying her narrowly, as if her dress was a surprise to him instead of a purchase he had supervised himself, overruling, with the approval of the shop's manageress, Tanya's own inclinations in almost everything. He had a very authoritative touch and she was not really surprised to find his taste impeccable, as the dress did suit her supremely well.

'It was very kind of you,' she faltered, strangely not feeling particularly grateful, but she couldn't stay silent for ever.

'Kind!' his exclamation was curt. 'I'm afraid I don't feel particularly kind, Tanya, but as you apparently like construing my motives as kindness, let me give you this. It strikes me that gratitude might be better than nothing.'

'No, Luke!' In horror she shrank away from him as, through the mirror of the vanity table where she sat, she saw him draw from his pocket the most fabulous necklace. It looked to her like that kind of necklace, a glittering length of extravagant diamonds, set with sapphires which exactly matched the dazzling blue of her eyes. The last days had done much to convince her that Luke Harrison was a man of some means, but it hadn't yet really sunk in. Not until this moment. 'My clothes and this hotel and everything would have been enough.' Her thoughts seemed to project themselves from shaken lips and he followed the line of them curtly.

'You're my wife now, remember.' His hands moved firmly on her bare skin as he guided the beautiful ornament round her neck and fastened the catch. 'There,' he said, more softly, 'don't you think you look good?'

'And anything you possess must look good?'

His eyes met hers through the glass, openly mocking. 'I don't possess you yet, but you're entitled to your opinions, of course.' His hands lifted from her shoulders as he stepped back, as if to survey the results of his handiwork rather than dwell on the pleasures she had so far denied him. Yet in his expression, as he noted her flushed face, lay a barely concealed derision.

'I'm sorry, Luke.' She felt the heat in her cheeks go right down through her whole body and strove to ignore it. The atmosphere between them wasn't good and might only deteriorate if she didn't make an effort. 'I do appreciate it. It looks magnificent.'

He inclined his head wryly. 'You could thank me properly.'

The implication behind his hard amusement was so plain she flinched nervously. 'You don't have to pretend you want that kind of thanks from me.'

She was unprepared for the strength of his hands on her shoulders again, hands which hauled her ruthlessly to her feet to face him. His eyes slaughtered her. 'Just what do you mean by that?'

Tanya hadn't meant to so much as mention the name again, but it was out before she could stop it. 'You still love Rowena, you can't deny it.'

'So we're back at that, are we? It's strange how women demand proof of love above all else.'

His eyes were like diamond chips. They should have daunted instead of stinging her to greater recklessness. 'So I'm asking the impossible?'

'Until you learn to trust me.'

'You think trust fertilises everything?'

His voice evened out laconically. 'You've a sarcastic little tongue when you like. Perhaps we should follow the earthy direction your remarks have taken? Who wants dinner anyway?'

He pulled her nearer and panic swamped her. She jerked her head back. 'Let me go, Luke,' she pleaded, her voice hoarse.

'No.'

'Please, Luke!' She tried to struggle, knowing the danger was real. She tried to stop herself responding as he slipped the light chiffon away from her shoulders and his head bent until his lips found her heated skin. Another minute, she sensed, might be too late. 'Listen to me,' her eyes suddenly blazed.

'One day I might, but not now, so you can scream as loud and long as you like,' he said tautly. 'You know you've had debts to pay for a long time.'

He was being hateful, frighteningly so, yet she couldn't stop her body from curving to the dominating pressure of his hands. His touch was like molten fire that he seemed to infuse into her very veins. When his mouth lifted from the pale curve of her neck to hesitate momentarily above her own, she opened her lips to receive the warm, deliberate hardness of his kiss. She tried to stop her arms from sliding up around his shoulders, her fingers from burying themselves in his dark hair, but her limbs seemed to have no thought of resisting but only of meeting his ruthless demands. Within her she was feeling, sharing the same urgent desire which motivated him.

'Tanya,' his voice sounded so harsh it shook her cruelly as his breath touched her cheek.

'You'd better let me go,' she repeated, gasping a little as she wondered where she was going to find the strength to deny him. Her soft mouth was burning, hungry.

'You're deluding yourself, little one.' As if her feeble protest induced violence, his arms tightened and the pressure of his mouth deepened to a hungry passion. Her hair came loose and he brushed it aside, murmuring something she was past hearing as his hand came down to explore her soft curved breast before sliding to her hip, moulding her against him until the hardness of his taut male body made her cry out. Still he kept on, the fire leaping, wiping away her inhibitions until all she wanted was to cling and cling.

It might have been a single tear that saved her, a silent unconscious protest against the innocence she seemed about to lose beneath the driving demands of his arms and mouth. The dampness was there against his face, seeming to act like a powerful deterrent.

'Oh, my God!' he said harshly. 'I can stand anything but that.' He looked down at her then thrust her suddenly away from him. 'I expect you're hardly ready for another emotional crisis, and I did promise.'

'Luke ...' He still had one hand on her arm as if, for all his caution, he was in two minds whether to let her go. He wasn't to know this time she was pleading for something else, that she couldn't bear him to leave her now—like this. She wanted him as much as he wanted her.

Her upturned face must have been very eloquent, but it seemed she was mistaken about his needs. He reached past her for the light wrap which lay on the dressing table. 'Come on,' he said coldly, draping it smoothly around her trembling shoulders. 'It's a woman I want, not a scared little icicle. We'd better have that dinner after all.'

CHAPTER NINE

TANYA never knew whether to look back on her honeymoon with regret or not. Viti Levu was a large island and with Luke by her side she might have been on a guided tour. He knew the island well and showed her over it in the most comfortable car he could hire, and she was still young enough to be curious and interested in everything. They drove over jungle-bordered roads, through narrow mountain gorges, rolling hills and deep valleys which descended to warm, sea-tossed beaches. He showed her sugar-cane plantations, rice-paddies and tapioca fields and drifts of bare brown earth ploughed by bullocks. Hotels were strung around the coast, interspersed by many of the island's villages. Many of these seemed to be populated by Indians. Luke told her that in the 1870s Indians were brought to Fiji to work in the sugar plantations and now there were more Indians than Fijians, the Indians dominating the commercial life of the country.

The crabs especially intrigued her. They were of all sizes and colour, ranging from pink to purple, red and black. There were large and small ones, some threaded on strings like beads and still alive. The largest were capable of climbing trees and crushing a coconut with their powerful pinchers. Others invaded houses by night, clattering through them when the doors were left open because of the heat and helping themselves to any tasty morsel they might discover. Crab stories in Fiji, Luke grinned, were as popular as fish stories in other parts of the world.

In other circumstances Tanya had no doubt she would have loved it all. As it was there were occasions when her enthusiasm seemed to bubble over, when she forgot her restraint in Luke's company and found herself laughing gaily, even becoming convulsed with girlish giggles. At

153

such times she imagined Luke sometimes lost his habitu-
ally hard expression and watched her with a slightly warmer
indulgence.

He didn't attempt to invade her privacy again but kept
strictly to his own rooms in the hotel, waiting usually for
her to join him in the lounge for a drink before meals.
Afterwards she sat idly on the veranda, which Luke seemed
to prefer to the beach in the moonlight or their private
sitting room, while he often talked to some chance acquaint-
ance in the bar or pursued agricultural and business papers.
It wasn't as if theirs was a normal honeymoon, he once
said cynically. It made her wonder, with a deep quiver,
what a normal honeymoon with Luke would be like.

So she watched the evening shadows lengthen and the
purple lines of other islands fade into the approaching
darkness as night fell over the sea, until it was time to go
to bed. During the day they either explored or lazed on the
warm coral beach and swam in the warm, clear waters. It
was a kind of earthly paradise, or could have been if her
relationship with her new husband had been slightly
different. As things were, Tanya longed to return to Luke's
home, which was now her home also. To be so near Luke
each day yet so distant was to her an intolerable if un-
explainable strain.

The day they came back to the island was one of those
burning days in the Pacific, when the sea is glassy but not
still, the swells coming up from the south unruffled by
any breath of wind but the huge heave of them telling of
storms not too far off.

As they landed in Luke's private plane the boom of
breakers could be heard for miles as they crashed on the
reefs. It wasn't a sound new to Tanya's ears. She remembered on Karowi how scared she had been, when
once they had caught the tail end of a typhoon, how it had
shaken the small island. Luke's island, by comparison, was
much larger but had still seemed a mere speck from the air,
crouched vulnerably between vast reaches of sea and sky.

Tui used to say, when Karowi shuddered, Tabakea

moves a little. Tabakea was a great turtle on the ocean bed who was supposed to carry an island on its back like a coral mushroom. One day Tui believed Tabakea would move too much and Karowi would topple over and be engulfed in roaring waters.

'Come on!' Half impatient, as if eager to be convinced the island had survived in his absence, Luke lifted her bodily from the plane and swept her towards the jeep. Soon they were out of the torrid glare, running through latticed palms towards the house, Luke's foot, pressed well down, ensuring that they arrived very quickly.

The sight of the house, standing as it did on the open plateau overlooking the great emptiness of sea, moved Tanya inexplicably, but her first glimpse of the hundreds of islanders who had turned out to greet them touched her even more. She was astonished to find almost everyone on the island was there to wish them well, including Luke's overseers. They were presented with many gifts and Tanya was decorated with colourful floral leis, garlands of beautiful flowers, while Luke stood indulgently by her, his hand on her arm.

One of the huge copra sheds had been cleared, and where before there had been great piles of dried coconut waiting to be collected by the next boat, a great feast had been laid on floor-level tables of banana fronds. There, beautifullly prepared, was every kind of island food imaginable, the *pièce de résistance* being a huge wedding cake. The feasting and dancing went on well into the night as, after the food disappeared, the copra shed became a dance hall. Tradition called for the bride and groom to dance first and Luke held Tanya in his arms and circled the floor several times while everyone agreed that the new missus was beautiful. Clearly Luke's wife was looked on with approval, and Tanya couldn't help wondering what they had thought of Rowena. Had she danced with Luke like this, held close in his arms? But, much later, when they returned to the house, to her surprise she found she had almost forgotten Rowena.

If being with Luke in Fiji had been almost unbearable, because of what she privately termed his distant nearness, here it seemed to become worse when she scarcely saw him at all. She had thought it was the quiet season and he did have a well trained, experienced staff, but he seemed busier than ever so that she rarely had much chance to have a proper conversation with him.

'The more affluent a man is the less his wife can expect to see of him,' Elizabeth assured her one day, her eyes sharp on Tanya's less than happy face.

Elizabeth was still with them, but Tanya didn't mind. In fact she was glad the sister hadn't yet sent for her. Elizabeth helped fill days which otherwise might have been empty, although some of her remarks were too astute to be wholly welcome.

'Where are the starry-eyed young modern brides?' Elizabeth's next remark startled her. 'You're a lovely girl, dear, but I imagined you'd be radiant.'

'Oh, have a heart, Elizabeth!' Tanya forced herself to laugh lightly. 'It's difficult to look anything in this heat.'

'It's been hot for days,' Elizabeth said severely. 'That's not the reason. It's more likely because you and Luke don't share the same room. I don't hold with these new-fashioned innovations.'

'Elizabeth, please!' Tanya flushed as she jumped to her feet. 'I know you mean well . . .'

'But I'm an interfering old woman and should mind my own business. I should also remember my place!'

'You know it's not that! We regard you as one of the family. We like having you around—joining us for dinner.'

'Luke shouldn't.' It seemed Miss Logan felt impelled to speak out at Luke's less than considerate treatment of the taut girl in front of her. 'A man with a new bride shouldn't want his old nurse sitting over him when he's newly married, or substituting almost every evening because he's not here.'

Tanya was relieved at that moment when Toma arrived to take Elizabeth to bed and, after they had gone, she sat for a long while just staring into space, as if visualising an equally empty future. It was quite dark outside and eventually she moved restlessly to the veranda, hoping Luke wouldn't be long. There had been news of a typhoon heading their way. The day had been so hot and unsettled, the sun baleful, like a great raging circle of fire. Before he had gone out Luke told her to stay close to the house, but this hadn't prevented him leaving himself. The wind was rising and she felt oddly on edge. What with this and Elizabeth's ramblings——! However did Elizabeth know that Luke had chosen to sleep in the small dressing room adjoining his larger bedroom that Tanya now had exclusively for her own use? Someone must have guessed. Was nothing sacred on these islands!

It was sheltered on the veranda, but out at sea there were sudden squalls, where the clouds were lit by flashes of vivid lightning which, fortunately, still seemed some distance off. A tropical storm could be like this, hanging around for hours. On the other hand it could strike suddenly, with a terrifying ferocity, filling everyone in its path with an unholy fear. Suddenly she felt she must go and meet Luke. He must be on his way as he was rarely as late as this, and she knew a sudden urge to see him. He couldn't be very angry, and anything would be easier to bear than just sitting here. She had dismissed Dino for the night. He had retired to his own quarters and wouldn't see her go. She wouldn't take the spare jeep, so no one would hear her either. This way it would be simple just to turn around and wander back if Luke didn't turn up.

Abstractedly she hitched the long, flimsy dress she wore over her arm. It was dark, but not so black that she couldn't see the track, and in her light attire Luke couldn't miss her. There was no fear of the dark in Tanya's heart as she was well used to wandering alone on Karowi, always finding the coolness of the later hours a blessing after the blazing heat of the day. The North Star had vanished and she couldn't see any of the others. At any other time this might have struck her as strange, as the stars here were never obscured by dust or haze, but this evening her thoughts were centred wholly on Luke as she tried to cope with a wild longing to be in his arms again, to be held tightly and kissed by him. Fiji seemed too long ago.

Tanya had gone some way before she realised the weather was indeed changing, and rapidly. No one could tell for certain how a typhoon begins, but once started it is impossible not to recognise. For unknown reasons the hot air of the tropics begins to spin and feeds in the surrounding air until it forms a vast whirlpool which can range up to a thousand miles in width. The revolving mass is then pulled along by upper winds until it mysteriously disperses or hits a land mass. The winds within a typhoon often reach well over seventy miles an hour and have been known to measure a hundred and fifty. One moment the winds will drop to nothing, the next instant they will roar by at incredible speeds. This fluctuation, Tanya knew, was what did most of the damage.

She realised, with the instinctive sureness of a small animal, that she must seek shelter right away. She was too far from the house, and as the first rushing wave of wind struck her she threw her bare arms frantically around the broad girth of a coconut tree. These were strong and deep-rooted, but there were branches crashing all around her. The wind was in her hair, flinging it in her eyes, tearing at her clothes and ripping the dress from her shaking shoulders. She doubted if she would ever be seen again alive—and she had never told Luke how much she loved him! When his jeep drew up violently beside her she thought it was lightning, as his lights blinded her, and she screamed wildly.

'You little fool!' If he had been an angel of mercy he couldn't have been more welcome, regardless of his scathing tones. 'What the hell are you doing here!'

The wind tore at her and she couldn't speak, only gasp ineffectually through terrified lips, as he took hold of her and she clung to him.

'We'll try and make the old workman's cabin in the cross

section,' he yelled, picking her up bodily.

'Home——' she managed to make the one word intelligible, and he shouted back,

'Impossible. There are trees down everywhere!'

'The jeep?'

'Suicide! Any minute it could go over. Now shut up!'

Tanya's dress ripped again, but she didn't hear it. The force of the wind was screaming and while Luke would have his work cut out getting anywhere, anywhere was safer than under a coconut tree where, in spite of its deep roots, they might easily be killed by flying nuts.

There came a lull in the wind, a merciful few seconds in which Luke moved with the swift, calculated stride of a panther. The pause in the mind-stopping cyclone was only that of a mighty giant drawing breath and strangely just as terrifying as its maniacal shriek. When the hut door flew open beneath the force of Luke's foot, Tanya almost sobbed with relief.

He didn't glance at her as he dropped her to the floor but turned immediately in an attempt to secure the door. Her actions purely instinctive, she thrust herself against it too, attempting to hold it as he groped for a heavy spar.

'It's not very good,' he shouted, wedging it into place, 'but it's the best I can do. We'll just have to pray it holds with the roof.'

Tanya dared not leave his side, her hands clinging to the tall, grey shape of him which was all she could make out in the lightning-splintered darkness. She could feel herself shivering from reaction. With what seemed to be only the remnants of her dress around her she felt cold, although this wasn't important. 'I'm sorry,' she cried, her voice almost lost under the battering roar of wind.

'It wouldn't have made much difference. I couldn't have made the house anyway.' Luke was pushing something big against the door, fixing the shutter on the small window. 'But you——!'

Words appeared to fail him and she was thankful of the dark so she couldn't see how he must be glaring at her.

She had been foolhardy, running out the way she had, leaving Elizabeth. A new apprehension shot through her. 'The house, Luke? Elizabeth!'

He held her steady as the hut rocked. 'There's a lot of teak there. The house creaks and groans a bit, but it will stand, and Elizabeth's used to this kind of thing.'

'The plantation?'

She thought his voice sounded harsher, but he only said, 'If we're lucky we'll just catch the edge of it.'

It was exhausting to shout above the noise of the wind and thunder-driven rain as she tried to find something else to hang on to when Luke left her to try and improve on the battens already behind the swaying door. He muttered beneath his breath things she pretended not to hear.

She was wet through, though no longer cold, and she felt uncomfortable. The cabin shook and there was fear in her heart as she listened to the racing drag of the tornado that swept everything from its path; the downward menace of its long arms which could crush and batter with maniacal force. What her fate might have been if Luke hadn't found her she shuddered to think.

When the first big tree hit the cabin she thought the roof was going and thrust a tight fist against her mouth to prevent herself screaming. She was scarcely aware that Luke had hold of her again, his arms tight around her, taking her ruthlessly with him as he almost dived beneath something that looked dimly like a large, heavy table. Bits of thatch fell all about them and the din was incredible.

Luke confirmed that they were under a table, when he got his breath back. 'It's old but solid. If the roof goes it might save us.'

How long he held her while the wind battered unmercifully Tanya didn't know. It seemed possessed of all the demons of hell, bent on taking them back there with it. With each fresh lull she shivered, with every new onslaught she tensed and trembled and his arms tightened protectively, his lean hard body shielding hers. It was strange, she puzzled numbly, how one could be in such a position, in such circumstances, yet be scarcely aware of it.

'Luke ...'

'Yes?'

'We could both die.'

'We could,' he teased, yet she thought she detected an underlying seriousness, as if he was as aware as she was of what could happen.

Another tree crashed and although it didn't hit them this time, the noise was again deafening. She clung to him, sobbing, thinking wild, crazy thoughts. 'I've never truly been your wife.'

'No, you haven't.'

She hadn't realised she had spoken aloud, nor that she could experience such a hot flood of embarrassment. The storm must be affecting her brain and it seemed he could be laughing at her, the way he agreed with everything. 'You don't have to poke fun at me, Luke. Not like this, not here!'

He mightn't be actually laughing, but he sounded full of a dry mockery. 'You wouldn't be offering yourself, by any chance? A kind of sacrifice to the gods, for your sins?'

'You're beastly!'

'Or is it just that you'd feel deprived, dying without knowing?'

She was sobbing in earnest now, seeking wildly to escape him, but he only laughed harshly and bent his mouth to the throbbing pulse in her throat. It was as if the idea had taken hold of him, too, and she quivered as his arms crushed her ruthlessly. His shirt, like her dress, was practically non-existent and, as he moulded her body to his, it was like wet silk on naked flesh.

He asked, lifting his mouth a fraction to trail her cheek, 'You want to make amends, perhaps, for the nights you've lain in your big comfortable bed and never spared me a thought?'

'It wasn't like that, Luke!'

'But you never guessed how I felt—aching for you.'

'Not loving me, though?'

'What has that to do with it?'

A fresh tear ran down her face, mingling with the others. 'Any woman would have done . . .'

'Possibly, but you got rid of them all, did you not, my busy little wife? You should be more than willing to compensate.'

Was he still mocking—or holding a sword above her head? He could be both, and the new weakness invading her body didn't help.

His voice was deep against her ear, as if he made sure she would hear. 'If there's one chance in a million we wouldn't come through this, I want you to know I'd like to love you completely.'

She shivered as his hands pushed the remaining wet rags from her shoulders, unable to reply through the sweeping force of her own longing. It was as if the storm directly aided him with its violent abandonment. There was a curious rending sound, as if the whole of the cabin was coming apart, and she screamed—a scream which was cut off by the silencing force of Luke's mouth against her own, and it was as if the passionate wildness of the night enclosed them completely.

'Luke . . .' She had no thought now of denying him anything as her own desire rose, as tumultuous as the hurricane. She clung to him, her eyes heavily closed, feeling his lips crushing hers before they wandered, to explore with insistent passion the hollow cleft between her breasts. His hands moved, with firm deliberation, a drugging expertise which soothed the last tension from her slight body, until every last bit of caution was gone.

That they might be using the storm as an excuse didn't occur to her. Feeling rose between them beyond description, a warm passionate tide which brought small inarticulate sounds to her tight throat and caused her soft warm hands to shape the nape of his neck. She seemed to have no thought of resisting, only of meeting his ruthless demand.

He pushed her further under the canopy of the table, sliding with her to safety, and her hands were as urgent as his as he pulled her down beside him. There was only the darkness of the elements above them, drawing them into a whirlpool of devastation, spinning them out into fiery space. Tanya could feel herself hurtling, then floating as his heavy masculine body crushed hers and the pressure deepened to unbearable pain before light struck so brilliantly it swept her magically upwards and she heard her own voice saying Luke's name again and again. He didn't spare her as in other, saner circumstances he might have done. It was as if, at the last moment, his control went and she was taken savagely with him towards the very stars.

Later, when the storm died away, he carried her back to the house. She protested, but only faintly, because her legs felt so weak and she knew that with his great strength he would scarcely notice her weight. She didn't know how long they had been in the rough cabin, but she knew she would always think of it as a beautiful place, a place she would remember with rapture all her life.

Luke didn't speak until they reached the house, and Tanya didn't try. With a new humility she considered his mind was already trying to assess the damage around them and that the night, for him, was something that must be mixed with regret. It was still not light enough to see the whole extent of the destruction, but she had little doubt that, even if they had got off lightly, there would be enough of it.

Dino was dramatically glad to see them, chattering excitedly in a language she didn't understand. The house was untidy with dust and leaves and pieces of the lighter furniture toppled over, but nothing seemed irreparably broken. Dino explained, when she asked him, that the front door had blown open several times, scattering many things in the huge hall. The servants had been busy, but some had been too frightened to be of much use. The other end of the house, the older part over the kitchen quarters, had suffered most, he thought.

Miss Elizabeth, he nodded, had been disturbed. She had asked for Tanya and when it was found she was missing was very upset. They had searched the whole house for the little missus and had all prayed she would be with the boss when she couldn't be traced. Miss Elizabeth had declared all along that she must be with Luke.

Luke didn't put Tanya down but carried her straight upstairs. The jeep hadn't been blown over, but the track was so blocked with trees it had been impossible to move it. Luke had found a coat inside and Tanya had slipped gratefully into it. 'It makes me look respectable again, not that I feel that any more,' she had tried to say lightly, and only succeeded in flushing painfully.

Luke had grinned, if rather grimly, 'You're a married woman, Mrs Harrison.'

He left her in the bedroom and went to run her a hot bath himself. 'Straight in,' he said firmly.

'Oh, Luke . . .' she glanced at him helplessly, not knowing quite what to make of his suddenly forbidding face. 'I don't want you to make a fuss. I'm sure I haven't caught cold.'

'That could be the least of your worries,' he cut her off curtly. 'It's been a devil of a night, in more ways than one, and not yet finished. I've a lot to see to, so do as I tell you like a good girl. After your bath get straight to bed. If Elizabeth needs you I'll come back for you, but I doubt it. As I said, it's not her first typhoon by a long way.'

He was curt, unsmiling, even when she smiled at him palely, and she had thought he would be different—after tonight. She wouldn't let herself think about it, however, as she bathed and wrapped herself in a thin robe before, contrary to his orders, she ran to see if Elizabeth was all right. First things first! She could relive Luke's love-making, or rather the memory of it, later.

Elizabeth was sleeping quietly, with Toma stretched out on a makeshift bed on the floor. It all seemed very peaceful after the storm.

'Boss say to stay here tonight,' Toma whispered. 'He has gone to the villages to see if anyone hurt. I hope nobody get hurt, Missus Luke?'

Tanya hoped not too, and wished she had gone with

him to see if she could have helped. She said so aloud.

'No,' Toma hastened, 'Boss not want you out there again. He give orders you must rest. There will be enough people to help.'

When Tanya returned to her room she found Dino had left a tray with hot drinks and she hastily swallowed some coffee before tumbling into bed. She tried not to worry about Luke while unable to think what she would do without him—now, if anything should happen to him. It seemed more sensible to suppose that from the way he had come through the storm, he was well able to look after himself.

She fell asleep and woke with a start an hour later to find him bending over her. 'Luke?' Lovingly she raised a hand to touch his cheek. Dawn was just breaking, she could see the first pale light creeping through the window. While she slept Luke must have come in and she hadn't heard. He must have been quiet, but he had obviously bathed and shaved, the dampness still clung to his hair and he wore his pyjama trousers.

'I can't stay,' he said, in a low voice, his dark eyes meeting hers enigmatically. 'I just came to see if you were all right. You shouldn't have woken up.'

'I'm glad I did.' She blinked sleepily up into his hard, handsome face, sliding warm arms around his neck.

'Tanya. I've to go out again.' He lifted his hands quickly to try and free himself. 'There's been a lot of damage. No one badly hurt, but a lot to see to.'

The dim light seemed to find her suddenly tormented gaze. 'Please, Luke.' Something uncontrollable was taking hold of her and she knew a small shiver of shame. It still didn't come naturally to plead, especially when her eyes must be plainly telling him she wanted him to love her. Her eyes were more tormented than she realised, as she somehow moved closer, and she was not able to see what she looked like with a faint colour pulsing beneath her satiny skin, her thin, sensuous body in the silky nightdress.

He groaned aloud, 'This is madness, and you must know

it, Tanya,' but the smouldering restraint at the back of his eyes blazed into something else before such fragile seduction. His hands, instead of unclasping hers, shifted deliberately to encircle her and the bed gave as his weight came down beside her. 'You must have been designed to drive a man insane,' he muttered, drawing her to him urgently, his hand closing tightly over her quivering breast while his mouth found hers. 'I guess they can do without me for another hour or so,' he added thickly.

The next time Tanya woke he was gone, but she lay still, drowsily content, scarcely aware of the ache deep within her limbs. Luke loved her. He had made no secret of his hungry passion and his lovemaking had been a revelation. Together they seemed to span dizzying heights. He couldn't surely make love to her like this if he didn't care. For her it would have been impossible if she didn't love him deeply. Although she still had to tell him so, she must have betrayed herself in a dozen ways. There might be no need for such a confession even while she intended making it. He must have guessed; the completeness of her giving could have left him in little doubt.

She rose at last, half ashamed of her continuing lethargy. It was strange that in spite of the storm and its aftermath she should be feeling alive as never before. Taking a quick shower, she slipped into a fresh cotton dress then ran along to Elizabeth's room.

Elizabeth wasn't there. When Tanya found her she was down having breakfast, eating her toast as if the dreadful night had never happened, outwardly as perky as ever. There was no sign of Luke, but then he would be out, naturally.

Tanya smiled uncertainly as she poured herself some coffee. 'I'm sorry about last night, Elizabeth. I'm afraid I didn't stop to think before I went out, but I shouldn't have left you.'

Elizabeth looked her over keenly, noting the pink cheeks, the sparkle which made sapphire eyes dazzling. 'It wasn't my first storm, dear. It was you whom I was worried about.'

'I went to meet Luke. I only intended going a little way. I was restless.'

'I suspected as much, but I didn't know that you had found him. I could only hope you had, and pray.'

Tanya dreamily contemplated her coffee, her face unconsciously flushed with a soft radiance.

'Storm or no storm,' Elizabeth commented, 'you look very happy this morning.'

Tanya's flush deepening, she was unable to stop herself saying impulsively, 'Luke and I discovered we love each other last night.'

If Elizabeth considered this a rather odd remark for a newly married girl she gave no indication. 'Some good always comes of the worst things,' she said cryptically, 'I'm very pleased.'

'At least,' Tanya's rapture modified a little and after the relief of telling someone, she tried to be honest, 'I discovered how much I love him.' The sudden doubtful thought struck her that Luke had never actually said he felt the same way. 'I think he loves me too ...'

'If he doesn't already, it will soon follow, child. If you're a good wife to him.'

'I'm going to try!' Tanya promised feverishly.

Elizabeth nodded, 'Any woman Luke Harrison loves can count herself very fortunate indeed.'

Elizabeth was watching her with a mysterious mixture of approval and concern, under which Tanya stirred restlessly. She put down her coffee cup quickly, afraid she had said too much. 'I think I should go and find Luke, see if I can be of any assistance.'

'Oh, I shouldn't, my dear,' momentarily Elizabeth looked startled. 'You wouldn't get through, in any case. Luke knows his way around, but there are so many trees down you'd only come to grief—and that wouldn't help!'

'But I feel I should go. After all, I am his wife.'

Tanya said it as if she had only just discovered it, and Elizabeth smiled. 'I shouldn't worry too much. When Luke comes back he'll soon let you know if there's anything you can do.'

Luke did not come back until early the next day. It was some time after midnight before Tanya heard him come in and, meanwhile, something happened to make her wonder if she ever wanted to see him again.

After breakfast and talking to Elizabeth she had changed into a pair of jeans, intending to keep as busy as possible. There had been enough to do, what with litter to be tidied away and repairing some of the minor damage left by the typhoon. Usually they had enough servants to cope with the ordinary daily tasks, but an emergency such as this pushed everyone to the limit. Tanya didn't notice how Elizabeth looked on her efforts with approval, nor how Dino and the others glanced at her with a new and affectionate respect.

One of the reasons Tanya worked so hard was that it prevented her worrying too much about Luke. Rumours came through, but that was all. One man he sent said, when he arrived, that one of the villages had been almost completely blown apart and many of the people had to be rehoused. Tanya thanked the man and sent him back with the message that they were managing and didn't need extra help.

During the early afternoon, to her surprise, the telephone rang. She had not given it a thought, imagining that after the storm it would be out of order. Her surprise turned to dull dismay when she realised it was Rowena, on the radio link from Australia. Tanya had thought it might be Luke.

'Is Luke there?' Rowena asked, after giving her name.

'No,' Tanya faltered, forgetting to say she was sorry. 'No, he's not.'

'I heard you'd caught the tail end of the typhoon and was anxious to know if he's all right. I suppose it's Tanya?'

'Yes.'

'I knew you were home again.'

'Obviously,' Tanya managed to reply, this time with a little more spirit. She had tried not to wonder how Rowena had known they would be back so soon.

'Luke told me.' Was Rowena a witch that she had been

able to read Tanya's thoughts? 'He said he'd be glad to get home when he spoke to me from Fiji. He rang me.'

'I see.' Tanya had dropped the receiver as though it was a hot brick, not caring that Rowena might be still speaking.

Luke had sent another message, this time to say he didn't know what time he would be back and not to wait up for him. Rowena's call had been a shock, Tanya couldn't pretend otherwise, not even to herself. She had not seen Rowena since Luke had arranged their marriage, nor had she wanted to. She had decided it would be wiser to try and forget her and had imagined she was succeeding. She had thought Luke was forgetting her too—until this! That he had talked to Rowena from Fiji seemed like a betrayal.

For all this, Tanya tried to be honest. There had seemed little enough, she was ready to admit, between Luke and herself on their honeymoon. He had probably felt quite free to do as he liked, even to contacting Rowena. He needn't have said he would be glad to be home, though. That bit hurt most. It almost hurt more to be forced to face up to one's own incredible naïveté. Just because Luke had made her properly his wife it didn't prove he loved her— that had been her own foolish conclusion, one he was probably laughing at right now. He could intend using her simply to satisfy his physical passions. Perhaps not even this, when he had had time to consider.

Unhappily Tanya had dragged herself to bed, hoping fervently to obliterate her misery in unconsciousness. When sleep didn't arrive she vowed she would pretend it had when Luke did come in. But when he did, it was not to her room he came. She heard him in the small room next door, the one she had thought he would never use again.

She didn't move but lay clenching her perspiring hands, rubbing them feverishly over her hot brow. He would be tired, this must be why he had gone in there, but surely he would at least look in? Or was he deliberately keeping out of her way, already regretting what had happened between them, putting it all down to emotions foolishly aroused by the storm?

Tanya held her breath as she heard the soft creak of his bed, then found suddenly she could stand it no longer. It was like a fever eating into her. It was impossible to lie here, let alone sleep. Maybe Rowena had deliberately set out to make mischief? Tanya bit her lip doubtfully. Perhaps if she swallowed her pride and showed Luke she cared he would reassure her about everything. He might even have discovered he loved her since they had returned from Fiji. On the other hand, if he did not, well—wouldn't it be better to know?

Quickly she picked up a comb, running it lightly through her tumbled hair. Then, after pulling a silk negligee tightly around her narrow waist, she walked slowly across the room and opened the door.

CHAPTER TEN

As soon as Tanya opened the communicating door Luke practically ordered her out. He might well have done, so unenthusiastic was his welcome. He hadn't gone to bed but was sitting, still in his shirt and pants, on the edge of it. There was a drink in his hand and a sheaf of papers by his side, although he did not appear to be giving them much attention. His glance, as it went swiftly over her, was so grim she might have been a stranger. Nor was his voice exactly friendly either.

'Tanya! What on earth do you want at this hour?'

'Want?' Her newly aroused emotions were so sensitive as to be frozen immediately by his expression alone. It turned his curt question into an insult. She took a wounded step backwards, which only seemed to add to his irritation.

'For heaven's sake, Tanya, I've had quite a day! A hysterical scene is something I don't feel like facing.'

'I'm sorry.' Her eyes were anguished, but he didn't seem to notice. She made a great effort to copy his coolness. 'I didn't come for—for what you think.' Stopping abruptly, she flushed scarlet, not altogether sure this was absolutely true. She put up her two hands to hide her hot cheeks before rushing on, 'I came to see if you were all right and to say I'm sorry about the damage and everything. I've been worrying, we all have, wondering how the rest of the island fared.'

'Have you?' Clearly he didn't altogether believe her. 'I suppose it should be comforting to have a wife capable of considering such matters at this time of night, but I repeat, I've had one hell of a day!'

'So have I!' Because he jeered some of her anxious self-effacement seemed to leave her. Her sapphire eyes widened, tears glistening on her darkening pupils, making them sparkle like dew-drenched jewels, but when she felt like running, some streak of obstinacy kept her glued to the spot.

For a moment he stared intently, then his lip curled. 'Doing what?'

All caution fled beneath his cool, hard look. 'Answering your phone calls, for one thing. You can consider this the main reason I'm here. To tell you——'

'Well?' he prompted brutally as she faltered, biting her lip. 'You could have left a note downstairs if it's all that important. Or are you making it up? It wouldn't be the first time a woman has found an excuse to invade my bedroom. Usually I'm flattered.'

Tanya was stung to instant fury, an anger that dispersed a little of her unhappy bewilderment. How dared he class her with those other women, with whom he had undoubtedly achieved the degree of expertise which made him such a satisfactory lover! Tightly she closed her eyes against the enormity, the memory of that!

'It was Rowena,' she explained.

'Rowena!'

For a second Tanya thought he was about to add something uncomplimentary and a little of the constriction eased around her heart. With his next sentence, however, she realised she was completely mistaken.

'How nice,' his white teeth glinted in a pleasant smile. 'I'm sorry I wasn't here.'

Tanya went white. She would liked to have thrown at him what Rowena had divulged about Luke ringing her from Fiji, but somehow she couldn't. The doubt she had regarding the veracity of that was small but was the only bit of comfort she had to hang on to. If she told Luke exactly what Rowena had said and he confirmed it, she didn't think she could bear to stay here any longer. Nor would she feel she had any excuse to, in spite of being married to him. As things were Tanya wondered if there was anything left to fight for.

'Perhaps you should have married Rowena again instead of me,' she cried, hurt to her very soul.

'But I didn't.' He shrugged, appearing entirely indifferent, his mouth curling again. 'Neither am I contemplating a second divorce, if this is what you're looking for. Not yet. Now go to bed. I'll get in touch with Rowena as soon as possible. Thanks for telling me, anyway.'

Picking up his glass, he swallowed the remaining contents in one go. He lifted the sheaf of papers as if ready to pursue them, running an impatient hand around the back of his neck, reminding her of the way he had forced her head around to his last night when he had begun making urgent love to her. Swiftly she cut off such thoughts, but even to let them into her mind had been a mistake. They held her immobile, staring at him, her huge eyes reflecting clearly her anguish, her hunger.

'Tanya! In heaven's name!' Suddenly he was on his feet, across the room, his hands clamped tight on her shoulders. To feel her obviously shaking under his grip apparently aroused him only to fury. His eyes berated her, his tongue lashed. 'It makes me sick to see the way women beg! Where's your pride, girl?'

'Luke ...!'

'Don't Luke me! I had enough last night. And if you wait a day or two you'll thank me for not taking advantage of something that should never have happened. It might interest you to know I like my women more mature. Maybe one day you'll grow up a little.'

It was worse than anything she could ever have imagined. He made a mockery out of everything she would have held sacred. It was like a douche of cold water, only water never induced this kind of pain. What had he said about pride? Stiffly she held herself away from him, but while his fingers continued to burn through the thin silk of her robe it was a shattering achievement.

'I'm sorry, Luke,' she managed at last, 'I think I've been wrong about a lot of things. Now I can see clearly, and if it's too late to make amends at least I can keep out of your way. You must certainly have been amused by me last night, in spite of the ravages of the storm. From now on you must feel free to do as you like—with whom you like.'

'Tanya ...'

But she was wrenching away from him, expending the last of her strength. Whatever he had been going to say, after that last exclamation was torn from him, she didn't want to hear. She couldn't take any more of his anger, his taunting, humiliating remarks. Her bedroom door shattered behind her as she flung herself over the bed, but for the first time in her life she found no relief in burning tears.

The following days seemed to Tanya grey in colour, all of them, for all the returning blueness of sea and sky. From the latter the sun blazed down as if the storm and its aftermath had never happened. After their bitter quarrel in Luke's bedroom she had been well aware of the faint hope at the back of her mind that he would seek her out and apologise, confess that he had been too tired to know what he'd been saying. This she could have understood as he had not been to bed in two days. When no such apology materalised she realised she was merely being stupid. He had such superb strength and control, probably half a dozen tornadoes would never affect him. Certainly it soon became quite obvious that he did not intend holding the storm responsible for any of his subsequent behaviour.

She didn't understand it, not entirely, and the more she tried to sort it out the more confused she became. It was ironic that she had fallen in love with Luke desperately and had hoped he was beginning to feel the same way. While Rowena's telephone call had been a shock, Tanya felt Rowena was someone he had put behind him, especially in view of what had just happened. Last night Tanya knew that if he had chosen to make love to her again she couldn't have stopped herself responding completely. It tore her heart, having to face the fact that he clearly regretted everything that had taken place bettwen them and wanted as little as possible to do with his new wife.

For a few days she had tried to be friendly, hiding her hurt, the pain of his rejection behind a deliberately bright face, but it had made no difference. Mostly he ignored her, obviously feeling he had no need to be more than distantly polite. She flushed afterwards with shame to recall how, on one or two occasions, she had been deliberately noisy when getting ready for bed, dropping things and humming a catchy little tune half under her breath. But she might well have done nothing for all the notice he took.

That episode hadn't lasted long as it went entirely against her nature to seek attention this way. Even to do it delicately seemed degrading. After several nights of being ignored and of weeping silently into her pillows, she packed up her clothes and retired to her old room, not caring what the servants might think.

She told Luke quite frankly what she had done, even managing to make a little joke out of it. 'You won't be so cramped now,' she said, her smile a masterpiece of deception.

'Just as you like,' he had replied harshly, not even bothering to glance at her, so that her smile had been wasted effort.

The island very quickly returned to normal. The typhoon had only caught one side of the island and blown itself out as it hit colder seas. The damage, though extensive, was nothing Luke told her to what he had sometimes seen on other islands. Once a friend of his had had his whole rubber plantation devastated and been ruined. Tanya had visited the injured and learnt quickly how help must be organised for everyone who needed it. No one was left uncared for and gradually the excitement and distress died down and was forgotten. The islanders were quick to smile again; only Tanya seemed unable to forget.

It was over two months later when Elizabeth went. Her sister, suprisingly renewed after her operation, came to collect her. Tanya was glad of a change of company as she hadn't felt well for days. It must be the sun. Perhaps it was too strong for her? She forgot how completely she had always loved it and seemed to thrive in the heat.

'You're looking pale, dear,' said Elizabeth, on the morning of her departure during breakfast.

Luke was there, an honour, Tanya guessed, for Elizabeth as she was leaving. He glanced at Tanya sharply. 'You've been swimming too much,' he said curtly, making her realise he must be aware of her early morning wandering on the beach. All those times she wasn't able to sleep.

'Probably,' she shrugged, not because she felt like agreeing with him but realising it must be something.

'Don't go again for a few days,' he commanded, his eyes still fixed on her, as if noting, as he hadn't before, the violet shadows under her eyes, the slight droop to her childishly curved mouth.

'I'm all right!' It was her turn to speak sharply, although she didn't look at him. He needn't pretend to be concerned when he often never so much as glanced in her direction for days.

Elizabeth embraced her warmly. Luke was flying the two ladies to Fiji where they would take a jet to the mainland. and he was doing a last routine check on the plane. 'Remember,' Elizabeth repeated firmly, 'if ever you need me you have my address. If ever you would like to come and stay my sister and I would be delighted to have you.'

Tanya waved wistfully as the plane took to the air. She had refused to go, although Luke had asked her. Somehow she couldn't face Fiji again. Hadn't she vowed she would never return to Viti Levu until she and Luke were completely happy? That day seemed unlikely to come now, she decided, a fatalistic conviction eating at her heart.

The house seemed too empty to bear when she went back to it, so she wandered down to the shore. Having promised Luke she would not swim while he was away she had every intention of keeping her word, but she found the gentle wash of the sea soothing and saw no reason not to walk beside it. As almost always she had it to herself, something she was thankful for when, minutes later, she was violently sick. It was some time before she was able to pull herself together, to find the strength to drag herself under a leafy palm and face a few facts. There was an uncomfortable nausea that seemed to be growing worse each morning, although today she had tried to control it until the others had gone. There was also a prevailing lethargy which too often seemed to consume her usual bright energy. A single tear escaped to run disconsolately down her smooth cheek as she realised with a very real bewilderment what was wrong. She had seen and heard too much of it in the islands where a family was regarded the natural outcome of marriage, and symptoms such as she was experiencing were looked on as normal and never hidden away under a cloak of foolish secrecy. Tanya counted the months, the normal functions of her body, and was forced to admit what for some weeks she had tried to ignore.

She might have cried, but she stared instead out at the ocean, dry-eyed with despair. She felt beyond tears, beyond everything. Luke, if he knew, would be furious. He would feel himself trapped, tied to a wife he didn't love, despite his desire for a son. It was possible he would allow her to stay because she was to have his child, but hadn't he once said he might be willing to keep such a child but not Tanya? Of course the law might not allow him to do this, but out here the planters seemed a law unto themselves. They were uncrowned kings of not inconsiderable territory and acted this way—and who was to gainsay them?

There was only one thing she could do, leave immediately. Luke must never know why. If she had a son he might have to. A boy might never forgive her if she robbed him of such an inheritance, but she might surely keep a daughter? It was important to think and plan, give nothing away. The islanders were astute. They might guess and tell Luke if given half a chance. It would be essential to be careful. Tanya rose slowly and walked back to the house, trying to formulate a plan from she didn't know where.

Luke was home the next night. He could have been sooner if he had not waited to see Elizabeth and her sister on to the plane. 'She sent her love for about the hundredth time,' he said, unexpectedly joining Tanya for coffee after dinner. He had the air of a man whose patience had been sorely tried. 'I assured her we'd be pleased to see her each year for as long as she cared to stay.'

'Oh yes.' Tanya smiled eagerly, forgetting her own worries long enough to sigh warmly. 'I quite agree. It will be lovely to have her.'

'You like her, don't you?' He stirred his coffee lazily, but his eyes were suddenly keen as they wandered over the girl sitting opposite, as if there was something slightly insubstantial about her that disturbed him.

'Why, yes.' Tanya was absolutely sincere and he knew it. 'She's really a darling and has most of her wits about her, in spite of what you said when I first came.'

'Yes,' he nodded teasingly, 'she all but offered to have her old job back, should the need arise.'

'No!' Tanya's cup almost toppled over as she jumped panic-stricken to her feet. Nerves stretched tight with the momentous discovery of yesterday, she stared at him, her cheeks growing visibly whiter. 'I ...'

Luke's own cup hit the glass-topped table as he swiftly grabbed her before she had a chance to escape. Holding her struggling, frantic body to him easily, he ground out grimly, 'So even to think of what that involves is repulsive!'

'No!'

Ignoring her small, anguished cry of protest, he pulled her closer, his face cold as his hands slid around her shoulders. 'I've a good mind to ...' Whatever else he had been going to say was lost as he lowered his head, crushing her lips with his in a long punishing kiss.

Tanya felt the same liquid flames that she had known before in Luke's arms surge through her veins, sweeping her along in a dizzying flood of longing. Passionate desire overcame her so fiercely and swiftly she thought she must faint from the white-hot radiance of it. As sensation pulsed between them, hemming them in, from her parted, too responsive lips came an odd little cry of despair.

It must have reached him and his mouth lifted from hers as he gazed down on her, noting her paleness. A harsh exclamation escaped the lips which only a moment ago had been devouring hers as if he never meant to stop. 'To so much as kiss me, now, fills you with disgust?'

She couldn't speak. She wanted to reassure him, but she felt terrible. If she didn't get away she might pass out, and then what might he not discover? Apprehension made her tremble as waves of nausea began hitting her again. 'I'm sorry, Luke,' she gasped, wrenching herself from his slackening grasp, her eyes more desperate than she knew.

'You still hate me, don't you?' He held her by one arm when she would have fled, and his voice rasped. 'Because I kept you here, forced you to marry me.'

'If you like.' She was past thinking. All she wanted was to get to her room before it was too late. He had such eagle eyes, he missed nothing. Sadly she proclaimed, 'You didn't actually force me to do anything, you simply advised me that it would be wise. I'm afraid your good deed has rebounded, since you discovered you still love Rowena.'

For a bleak moment he halted, as if he had for the first time in his life problems he wasn't sure how to handle. Then, before he could speak, Tanya jerked her arm and, feeling her flinch, he threw it from him. 'Run away,' he bit out, curtly sarcastic. 'I seem to have acquired the habit of saddling myself with the wrong kind of wives.'

All through the night Luke's words rang in her head until she felt she could scream with the pain of them. As dawn broke she fell to praying fervently that something might happen, some opportunity would present itself to enable her to get away from the island as quickly as possible.

To Tanya's surprise two things did happen which convinced her that her prayers had indeed been answered. Luke's brother had an accident and his distraught sister-in-law sent for him.

'I'd better go.' Luke frowned as he spoke to Tanya about it. 'I scarcely think Sara would send for me if it wasn't serious, but I could be gone a week. I don't like leaving you that long.'

Tanya's heart might have warmed if she hadn't known his remark was merely conventional. 'I could go with you,' she said. The atmosphere between them had been as strained as ever since Elizabeth left. It was back to rarely seeing him again, and while she might have tried to endure this the days were passing and she knew time was beginning to run out for her. As it was her figure was beginning to alter in subtle ways she was sure Luke must soon notice. Either he or somebody else. Only by getting off the island could she prevent this.

He might have read her thoughts as he refused to take her. 'You'd only be in the way,' he said.

He didn't add any more, but Tanya did. He neither wanted her nor was willing to let her go. No matter which way she looked at it, it was the only conclusion she could come to, and it hurt. She would like to have sent a message of sympathy to Sara and her husband, but what could she say to people she had never met? When she did say she was sorry, Luke shrugged carelessly and she doubted if he would remember to repeat it on her behalf.

She watched him leave with a strong feeling in her heart that she would not see him again, and when Captain James arrived with his copra boat she understood why. She would not have known he was there if Toma had not told her. The girl had been to the village, to which Luke had forbidden Tanya to go until he came back. That Tanya had not been there since he had left did not mean she intended obeying such stringent orders. She had stayed around the house because she had been feeling too ill to wander far. She had thought of going to visit the Browns, but had not done so as she was sure Edna Brown would mention Rowena. It was enough to know that Rowena was in Australia, that Luke would almost certainly see her while he was there. Tanya remembered the small dinner party she and Luke had given after their honeymoon for his executive staff, some of whom had flown in from elsewhere. The

Browns had been there and Tanya was sure that without Luke's surprisingly constant presence by her side she could never have hoped to hold Edna off.

When Toma came back and let slip that the copra boats had almost finished loading, Tanya didn't hesitate. Captain James would be there and she would make him take her to Fiji. Threaten or cajole if need be, she wouldn't give him a chance to refuse, and he had offered to help if ever she asked him.

While she threw the bare necessities into a small canvas bag she explained to a anxious, bewildered Toma that she was going to meet Luke in Fiji. She made it sound as if she knew exactly when he would be there, giving the impression, without resorting to lies, that he had told her himself when he had been in touch to say his brother was out of danger. Toma was not to know how Tanya felt driven to such deception.

She drove herself down to the loading docks, forcing herself to go slowly as she reached the copra sheds so that no one should be suspicious. In her mind was one fixed idea, overcoming all thought of bodily comfort. If she could get to Fiji she would decide where to go from there. One thing was certain, she vowed—Luke would never find her.

Surprisingly Captain James seemed to swallow her story as easily as Toma had done and in no time at all Tanya was installed in his own personal cabin.

'I'll move in with my great good-for-nothing first mate,' he boomed. 'It will just be for a couple of nights and only the best is good enough for my friends, especially when this one happens to be Luke Harrison's wife!'

Tanya knew he looked at her a little doubtfully, but she was grateful that he didn't ask any questions, though she had a peculiar conviction that he would have liked to, not being quite so gullible as he appeared.

It wasn't until they arrived in Viti Levu and she was saying goodbye that he openly tackled her. For two days the motion of the boat had kept Tanya unwell, this and the

sickly smell of copra which usually she was so used to she
never noticed. Her face was paler now than when she had
left the island and she looked ill.

'I did promise to help you,' the kindly captain growled,
'but you're sure you know what you're doing, ma'am?'

'Of course.' She dared not look him straight in the
eye.

There was silence, during which he sighed and stirred
uncomfortably. Then suddenly he was thrusting a wad of
notes into her hand. 'I know it's none of my business, child,
but I want you to take this. Something tells me you might
need it.'

'Oh, no . . .!'

When Tanya blinked and opened her mouth to protest,
he said gruffly, 'I have no one of my own, so you aren't de-
priving anybody. If you insist on repaying it, any shipping
office around here will find me, but I'd rather you considered it a gift rather than a loan.'

So she had been right, he had suspected something,
though he hadn't said anything. In a daze Tanya gazed after
his huge figure as he disappeared along the line of streets.
He had been so kind, treating her like an honoured guest
instead of a probably unwanted one, and now this!
Stunned, she stared down at the money in her hands. Didn't
he realise she might never be able to repay him?

During the next twenty-four hours she was grateful for
the sense of security this money gave her. She had a little
of her own which she had intended adding to by finding a
job until she had enough to buy an air ticket. Now, thanks
to Captain James's timely interception, this was unneces-
sary, but she still couldn't decide where to go. Elizabeth
would welcome her in Australia, and Tanya would have
chosen to stay either on Fiji or Australia, but was terrified
that if she did Luke would quickly find her. Eventually,
after a sleepless night, she realised there was only one
place she could go to, and that was back to England. The
following morning she took a taxi to the airport.

She did not anticipate getting away immediately, so she told the man to wait. The airport was busy, but she saw only a sea of faces. At the desk she was blindly groping in her bag for her money when a hand descended cruelly on her arm, literally halting the blood flow. For one aghast moment she stared down at it, knowing she would have recognised those long, lean fingers anywhere. She didn't really need to raise her eyes to see it was Luke.

The clerk behind the desk was waiting. 'The lady won't be taking a ticket after all,' Luke informed him, firmly removing Tanya's frozen hand from her bag before snapping it shut.

'I have to get a plane, Luke,' she gasped, her stunned gaze wavering. 'And I've a taxi waiting.'

'Where?'

'There.' As he swept her from the official buildings, away from the clerk's curious eyes, she pointed numbly.

Still keeping a tight hold of her, he strode over and tossed the man several bills. The tall Fijian thanked him profusely and drove off, as if the sight of a thin, sickly-looking girl in the clutches of a large, obviously bad-tempered planter was nothing unusual.

Tanya began to giggle, half hysterically, as it struck her how many things in this part of the world were accepted as normal. Things which in England might hit the headlines —'Furious man assaults helpless female,' she spluttered.

'Shut up!' Luke's rough shake dispersed the last remains of her false humour. It frightened her how he could, in effect, shake her almost without stopping as he dragged her towards his hired car. 'I warn you, Tanya, I've had about all I can take. Where are you staying?'

'How did you know I was here?' she countered, turning her head from him as he started the engine, so he wouldn't see how near she was to tears.

'Easy,' he returned harshly. 'I rang home yesterday. Troy had a brief relapse or I would have rung sooner to see how you were. Toma told me you'd come to meet me as arranged, but I knew that for the fiction it was!'

'I should have left here sooner . . .'

'So you should, if you really wanted to escape.'

'How did you know where to look?' Her voice shook as she realised that given another few hours she might have succeeded.

'The obvious place was the airport. I presumed you must have enough money. I've been cooling my heels, if not my temper, here all day.'

'I see.'

'Where are you staying? I don't want to have to ask a third time.'

'A small place.' She didn't want him to see how small.

'We're going back to settle and collect your things. I presume you haven't done this already?'

'No—I was going to before I left.'

'I'll do it now, then we'll get home.'

'No, Luke!' Suddenly what he was saying, what his formidable appearance meant truly got through to her. 'I can't go back to the island. I won't! Don't you see . . .'

'I see nothing,' he retorted, his voice like flint. 'We'll settle your bill and no more argument. If I hear one more word from you, God forgive me, I'll do something you won't forget in a hurry.'

Tanya didn't see any of the countryside as they drove to Suva and she numbly murmured the name of the quiet back street where she had found respectable but shabby lodgings. She had been quite satisfied, a sentiment apparently not shared by Luke, if his low exclamation was anything to go by.

His anger mounting, terse-lipped he told her to wait in the car, but she was outside before he could stop her.

'My things,' she gasped, feeling there must yet be some way she might evade him. 'I'm going to get them!' In a flash she was away from him, up the rickety stairs to the very top floor, trying to slam the door on him.

The trouble was his foot; she couldn't move it, and the force of his body following it spun her off her feet so that she landed in a quivering heap on the bare boards.

'Luke!' She felt awful. She stared up at him, tears blinding her.

'Tanya—I——' Then amazingly he was down on the floor beside her, gathering her up, his lips moving tenderly over her tear-damp cheeks, her stiffly held, trembling mouth. His mouth stayed on hers until he felt it relax and soften. Then he was holding her, kissing her passionately, as if he never meant to let her go. His arms crushed her, as he tightly held her slender body that seemed unconsciously to be seeking to get as close as possible to his.

'Tanya——' her heart leapt at his changed expression, 'didn't you guess how much I love you? You might not believe it, but I do.'

She lifted her eyes to look at him, her voice taut. 'You've forgotten Rowena.'

'What about her?' he asked, faintly dry.

'I thought it was Rowena you loved?'

His mouth twisted grimly. 'The feeling I had for Rowena was only mild infatuation compared with this! I could never let you go, so it's no use begging. I let Rowena go and never wanted her back, but you're completely different. I realise now that I never really loved her.' Tanya went tense as he added, 'Maybe one day you might come to care for me. God knows I'm prepared to wait long enough.'

Care for him! The words reeled through her head and she stared at him as if she couldn't be sure she had heard correctly. Didn't he know how much she cared already? And did he really mean it when he said he loved her? One glance at his face, the grey beneath his tan, the etched lines of strain around his mouth, convinced her. Her hands slid lovingly to meet around his neck and her eyes were revealing. 'If you knew how despairing I've been, you wouldn't need me to tell you how much I love you. I think I have from the beginning. I was mistaken in thinking it was hate.'

He looked down at her wryly and almost groaned. 'When Toma told me you had gone I think I nearly went mad! I tried to believe I was well rid of you, yet I knew life would scarcely be worth living without you. To hear you say you love me is like a miracle.'

She wanted to tell him then about the baby, to confess the true reason why she had left the island, but she could not find the breath, not while he was holding her so passionately. His mouth crushed hers again and she shuddered, the whole of her yielding and yearning as his hand found the warm curve of her breast and behind them his foot softly closed the door.

She was lost as he continued to kiss her with a driving intent, arousing her until she was wholly responsive to his need for complete fulfilment. Then he was putting her firmly away from him, controlling his urgent desire as a sweet tide of feeling rose almost irresistibly between them.

'You're so beautiful,' his lips touched her flushed cheeks gently as he drew her up beside him, lifting her into his arms once more, to drop with her into the only armchair the room boasted. His fingers trailed her silky arms. 'I want you all the time, but I've waited so long a little longer won't hurt me. In a couple of hours we can be back on the island.'

He made no immediate move but watched her bemused face intently. 'I've loved you a long time. I think possibly from when I first saw your so blue eyes staring at me through the cracks of your father's cabin.'

So many sensations were racing through her, but at this she was startled. 'Oh, Luke, I never guessed!'

He smiled sardonically. 'Why do you think I tried as hard as I did to supply everything you needed and bothered so much about your father's work?'

'And I wasn't even grateful!'

'Well. The trouble was your father died so unexpectedly, I hadn't even a plan. I felt forced to use Elizabeth in order to keep you on the island after you left Karowi. Then it seemed I had to almost force you to marry me. You were beginning to come between me and everything I did. That night I found you sleeping in my room I could simply have carried you back to yours and no one might have been any the wiser.'

'You let me stay?'

'So that you could become the whole of my life, not just part of it.'

Tanya said painfully, 'You must remember finding me in the library, looking through your cupboards? I asked Elizabeth if you had a photograph of Rowena. I must have been jealous, because I felt I would go mad if I didn't see her. Elizabeth thought you had some snapshots and I thought they would be there. When I couldn't find anything I decided to search in your room. I'm afraid I sat down on the edge of the bed to study Rowena's face and fell asleep.'

'You wondered why I kept that photograph, of course?' His eyes hardened. 'I kept it there to remind me what sort of a woman she was. It served as a kind of warning whenever I felt attracted to another.'

'I thought you still loved her.'

He shook his head grimly. 'Rowena and I married when we were little older than you, a marriage that seemed a mistake right from the start. She never settled on the island, she hated it. I hoped she would change, given time, but it only grew worse between us. I wondered afterwards if I should have been firmer. Maybe I was too young, but when I tried to improve matters by offering to live in Australia, she refused. She didn't want that, nor did she want a family either. Eventually she didn't even want to share a room. If I'd still cared I guess she could have made my life pretty grim, but as it was I'd ceased to love her long before that. When she asked for a divorce in order to lead her own life I only recall feeling relieved. I never saw her again until you were there and she paid that visit to the Browns.'

Tanya's voice shook slightly. 'You seemed friendly enough then.'

He said wryly, 'I may have hinted at something occasionally to try and make you jealous. Sometimes your apparent indifference, my darling, almost drove me around the bend! But I never said one word to her that might have given her mistaken ideas. Nor do I think, on her part, she ever really regretted our divorce. She's the kind of woman who's happier without a man, although she may still have dog-in-the-manger instincts.'

Surely he didn't expect her to laugh at that! Tanya's breath drew painfully, though she found with an easing of the constriction around her heart that she believed him. 'Before our wedding Rowena seemed to know exactly why you were marrying me.' The pain in her voice was audible. 'That was why I thought you didn't love me.'

She heard Luke say something beneath his breath. 'You believed her?'

'How else could she have known I was in your room?'

'Simply by putting a few rumours together and guessing the rest. I certainly never told her a thing.'

Luke's mouth tightened dangerously and Tanya knew she could discredit most of Rowena's other remarks. There was no necessity to recite them all. There was just one more thing before she put the unhappiness of the last weeks behind her. 'After the storm,' she faltered, 'when I thought everything was going to be all right, she rang me, remember?'

'Yes——' he prompted, drawing her closer, as if he remembered other, more important things.

For a moment Tanya resisted. 'She said you'd been in touch with her from Fiji, during our honeymoon. I felt terrible, and when you came in late and practically ordered me from your room I thought you didn't want me any more.'

The glittering fury in his eyes almost chilled her. 'My poor little girl,' he exclaimed, 'don't shrink from me! I'm furious with myself for ever exposing you to Rowena. I never got in touch with her from anywhere. In fact I did ring her after that and ordered her not to ring again, but if I'd had any idea she'd been telling you such tales I wouldn't have been so polite. That night, or was it morning, you came to my room all I wanted was to take you in my arms, but I felt I had to give you time. I seemed to have taken an unfair advantage of your youth and innocence. I realised that physically we were ideally suited, yet I was greedy. I wanted your love and respect as well and I thought there was only one way to get it. I guess I did it too clumsily.'

'Oh, Luke,' she whispered, tightening her arms about his neck to pull herself up and press soft little kisses against his cheek, 'I've been so miserable. I felt awful. I decided leaving you was the best thing I could do.' As he drew her closer, murmuring her name, she began to tell him about the baby, then stopped. She had news for Luke which she knew suddenly would delight him. Knowing of his love made her own feelings surge with a new confidence. She would tell him, but not until they were back on the island. Instinctively she was convinced there was only one place—at the house, after dinner, with the lamps turned low and the moonlight tracing silver fingers across the waters of the South Pacific. There she would tell Luke about his son. Tomorrow the whole island would rejoice, but she and Luke would have those first rapturous hours to themselves.

Pulling away from him, she jumped up from his kneee, her fingers curling tightly around his as he sought to restrain her. 'Come on, Luke Harrison, let's go.'

'Where?' There was something of his old teasing arrogance in his question as he came reluctantly up beside her.

'Home, of course,' she said, softly radiant, rising on tiptoe to press another swift kiss on his cheek. 'Home, darling. Home to our island.'

The Warrender Saga

The most frequently requested series of Harlequin Romances . . . Mary Burchell's Warrender Saga

Each complete novel is set in the exciting world of music and opera, spanning the years from the meeting of Oscar and Anthea in *A Song Begins* to his knighthood in *Remembered Serenade*. These nine captivating love stories introduce you to a cast of characters as vivid, interesting and delightful as the glittering, exotic locations. From the tranquil English countryside to the capitals of Europe— London, Paris, Amsterdam—the Warrender Saga will sweep you along in an unforgettable journey of drama, excitement and romance.

The Warrender Saga

The most frequently requested Harlequin Romance series

#980 *A Song Begins*

#1100 *The Broken Wing*

#1244 *When Love Is Blind*

#1405 *The Curtain Rises*

#1508 *Child of Music*

#1587 *Music of the Heart*

#1767 *Unbidden Melody*

#1834 *Song Cycle*

#1936 *Remembered Serenade*

Free *Special Bonus Offer*

Purchase all 9 Warrender Saga novels and receive Mary Burchell's We Followed Our Stars as a Free Bonus.

We Followed Our Stars is the story of two sisters who crossed the Atlantic in the golden days of the 1920s, plunging into the glittering world of the opera . . . and later into the horrible brutality of Hitler's war-torn Europe. It's the real story of Ida Cook, a stenographer who became one of the world's most loved writers of romantic fiction— Mary Burchell.

$1.50 *if purchased separately!*

Complete and mail this coupon today!